MULTIPLE CHOICE QUESTIONS FOR 'A' LEVEL PHYSICS

by **J. Marshall**, M.A.,

Head of the Physics Department,
Christ College, Brecon

T. B. Akrill, M.A.,

Head of the Physics Department,
Clifton College, Bristol

and **J. Q. Cosh**, Ph.D., B.Sc.,

Clifton College, Bristol

Edward Arnold

Answers

Answers to questions in this book are contained in the Answer Sheet for **Multiple Choice Questions for 'A' Level Physics** which is available, free of charge, to bona fide teachers on request to the publishers (The Education Department, Edward Arnold (Publishers) Ltd., Woodlands Park Avenue, Woodlands Park, Maidenhead, Berks., England).

Summary of Instructions

For easy reference while questions of different types are being attempted, a fold-out sheet giving a summary of the answer instructions has been pasted inside the back cover.

Answer Sheets

Time will be saved in checking and marking Multiple Choice Questions if suitable answer sheets are duplicated and handed out. A convenient pattern for these can be seen, used decoratively and, of course, enlarged, on the front cover of this book. The right-hand column can be used for recording correct answers.

First Published 1972
by Edward Arnold (Publishers) Ltd.
41 Bedford Square
London, WC1B 3DQ
Reprinted 1973
Reprinted with corrections 1974
Reprinted 1977, 1979, 1981

ISBN: 0 7131 2314 1

Printed in Great Britain by
Richard Clay (The Chaucer Press) Ltd.
Bungay, Suffolk

PREFACE

The authors have always felt the need for short questions to offer students in order to test their learning, understanding and intelligent application of physical principles. The increased popularity of objective test (coded answer) papers at A level has led to our collection being set in this form. The questions are for use *during* an A level course rather than at the end of it. They are not a series of A level papers but are arranged in twelve main sections which correspond to usual areas of teaching. The earlier part of each section contains questions which will help students to establish new ideas in their minds, while later there are a few tougher questions; these probe the understanding of the subject more deeply and should promote some discussion.

SI has been used throughout the text, in accordance with the booklet *Signs, Symbols and Abbreviations for use in School Science,* A.S.E., 1969.

Diagrams and graphs have been used very widely, most of these drawn by Dr. Cosh who is a qualified draughtsman. We find that such a presentation helps the student to grasp a question *and* to get at the physics.

Only limited skill in arithmetic is required in most of the questions. Sometimes the answer is simply ×2, ×3, ×4, etc., and in other cases the response is left unevaluated, as for example $15\pi/4$ s. In preparation, many questions which were originally numerical were either rejected or recast in graphical or algebraic form.

Three types of question are intermingled throughout the book, namely (i) multiple choice, (ii) multiple completion and (iii) assertion-reason. These are explained in the Introduction by means of worked examples, and a fold-out sheet at the end of the book provides instructions for answering each type. There are several different types of multiple completion/selection questions in common use; we have chosen a single set of answer codes. Every question in the book is answered **A, B, C, D** or **E**.

On the score of the assertion-reason type of question, it soon became evident that even among the authors there were differences in interpretation of the single word *because*. Some of these questions can be used to promote a lively debate, especially where the choice is narrowed to **A** or **B**. The authors themselves prefer **A** to **B** if the argument or logic is incomplete but otherwise valid. Despite difficulties we decided to include the assertion-reason type of question as we feel this is the only way to produce a coded-answer test for some important elements of the subject.

We should like to acknowledge the help given to us in the assessment of the questions by J. McMichael Esq., of The Edinburgh Academy, and A. McB. Collieu Esq., of Bradfield College.

Some adjustments have been made to the following questions in this reprint; **A19, A24, A75, B45, B54, C5, D24, D48, E6, E15, J4, J5, J30.**

J.M.
T.B.A.
J.Q.C.

March 1974

CONTENTS

INTRODUCTION

Three types of question are used throughout the book, namely

(i) multiple choice
(ii) multiple completion
(iii) assertion-reason.

The coding system used is such that the answer to *every* question is simply **A, B, C, D** or **E.**

ANSWER CODE

(i) *Multiple Choice*

This is the most straightforward type. Simply decide which *one* response is correct.

Example:

Here are five statements about E, the electric field intensity at a point. Which statement is *not* correct?

A E is a vector quantity
B E can be measured in N C^{-1}
C E is high where there is a high electric potential gradient
D E varies as $\frac{1}{r}$ in the region of an isolated point charge (r being the distance from the charge)
E E is always perpendicular to the surface of an insulated charged conductor

Plainly, the fourth statement is the faulty one, since E varies as $\frac{1}{r^2}$ and not as $\frac{1}{r}$.

Solution **D**

(ii) *Multiple Completion*

In this type four responses are given and numbered **1** to **4**. In contrast to the previous type one *or more* may be correct. The letters **A, B, C, D** and **E** are now used in the style of a formal code to indicate which selection of responses has been made, as follows:

A only **1, 2** and **3** correct
B only **1** and **3** correct
C only **2** and **4** correct
D only **4** correct
E only some other response or combination of responses correct

This code is to be used for *all* multiple completion questions.

Example:

Four identical, straight pieces of copper wire each undergo one of the following changes. Which will cause a rise in the resistance of the wire?

1 The length is increased, by careful stretching, from 4.0 m to 4.5 m

2 The cross-sectional area is increased by electrolytically depositing a thin layer of copper over its full length

3 The temperature is increased from 15 °C to 55 °C

4 The wire is coiled into a loose solenoid

The resistance will increase when the wire is stretched, fall when its cross sectional area grows, increase as it gets hot, and be unaffected when it is loosely coiled up. Responses **1** and **3** are correct therefore, and the code translates this as **B**.

Solution **B**

(iii) *Assertion-Reason*

The question now takes the form of two statements, linked by the word *because.* The reader must (a) decide as to the truth of the first statement (the *assertion*), (b) decide as to the truth of the second statement (the *reason*), and (c), if both are rated correct, decide as to whether there is the link between the two implied by the word *because.*

The letters **A, B, C, D** and **E** are now used again, in a rather different code to indicate the decisions reached, as follows:

A completely true

B assertion and reason both true, but the use of the word *because* is not justified

C only the assertion true

D only the reason true

E assertion *and* reason both faulty

This code is to be used for *all* assertion-reason questions.

Example:

A variable resistor is placed in series with a lamp and battery, and its value is increased steadily from zero to, effectively, infinity.

The power dissipated in the variable resistor climbs from zero at the start, and falls to zero at the end

BECAUSE

at the start the potential difference across it is zero, and at the end the current through it is zero.

The statement is completely true. A fully-stated argument would, no doubt, include a comment that the power is given by the product of the potential difference and the current, but the *reason* is both accurate and sufficiently convincing to warrant **A**.

Solution **A**

A summary of these answer codes appears on the flap attached to the rear cover, and is intended for ready reference.

A MECHANICS

Kinematics

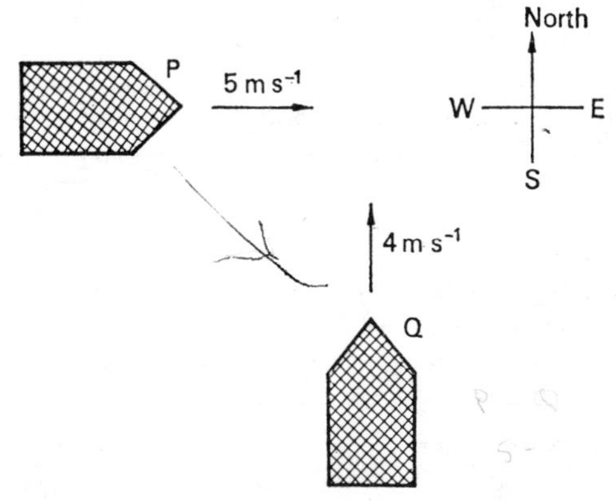

A1 P and Q represent two ships moving in a horizontal plane at the velocities shown each velocity measured relative to the Earth. The velocity of P relative to Q is

A $\sqrt{5^2 - 4^2}$ m s^{-1} in a direction which is very roughly NE
B $(5 + 4)$ m s^{-1} in a direction which is very roughly NW
C $\sqrt{5^2 + 4^2}$ m s^{-1} in a direction which is very roughly NW
D $\sqrt{5^2 + 4^2}$ m s^{-1} in a direction which is very roughly NE
E $\sqrt{5^2 + 4^2}$ m s^{-1} in a direction which is very roughly SE

A2 A golf ball, when driven off the tee, is reckoned to remain in contact with the clubhead for 5×10^{-4} s and to leave the tee at 70 m s^{-1}. Its mean acceleration while in contact with the clubhead is, to 2 significant figures,

A 1.4×10^{-5} m s^{-2} **B** 3.5×10^{2} m s^{-2} **C** 7.1×10^{2} m s^{-2}
D 1.4×10^{5} m s^{-2} **E** 3.5×10^{6} m s^{-2}

A3 A ball is rolled off the edge of a horizontal table at 4.0 m s^{-1}. (Take g to be 10 m s^{-2}.) We find it hits the ground 0.4 s later.

1 It hits the ground a horizontal distance of 1.6 m from the edge of the table
2 The speed with which it hits the ground is 4.0 m s^{-1}
3 The height of the table is 0.8 m
4 It hits the ground at an angle of 60° to the horizontal

A4 The graph shows the speed of a body against time.

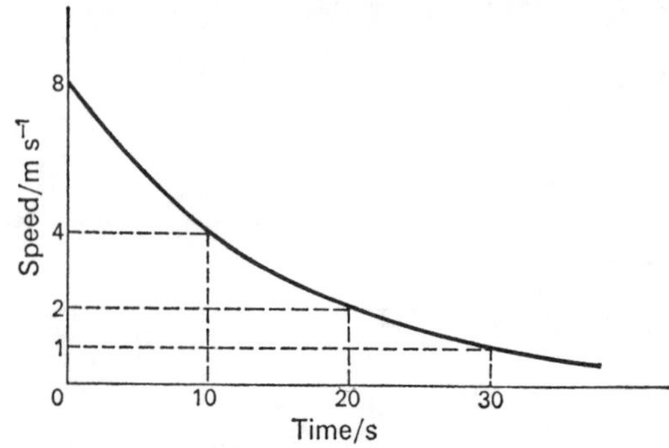

1 The speed of the body tends to zero
2 The average speed of the body tends to zero
3 The total distance covered will be finite
4 The time taken for the body to come to rest will be finite

A5 A particle undergoes a linear motion where its velocity varies with time. The first part of the motion is described by the graph. Using suitable scales for v and t, the motion described *could* be that of

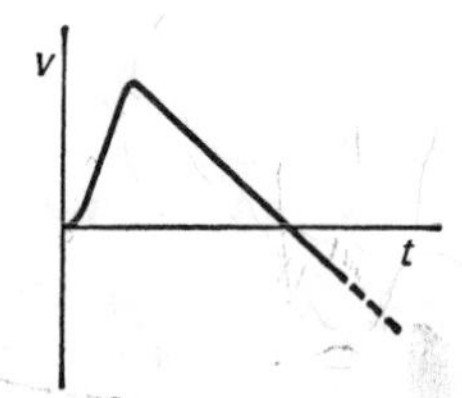

A a man sprinting 100 m from rest
B a ball thrown in the air
C a football kicked at a wall from which it rebounds at the same speed
D a ball, released from rest, rolling down a uniform slope
E a bus journey from one stop to the next

A6 A particle undergoes a linear motion where its displacement, s, varies with time, t, as shown. A graph of the particle's acceleration, a, plotted over the *same* time interval will look like

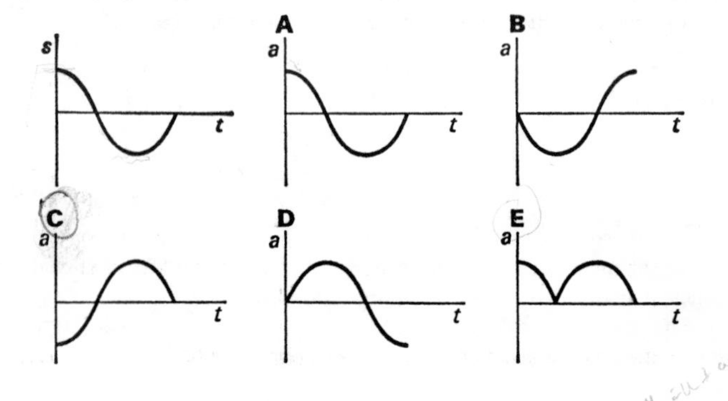

A7 A boy falls a short distance on to a trampoline and rebounds to his starting point. Which graph shows the variation in his vertical acceleration, a, with time, t?

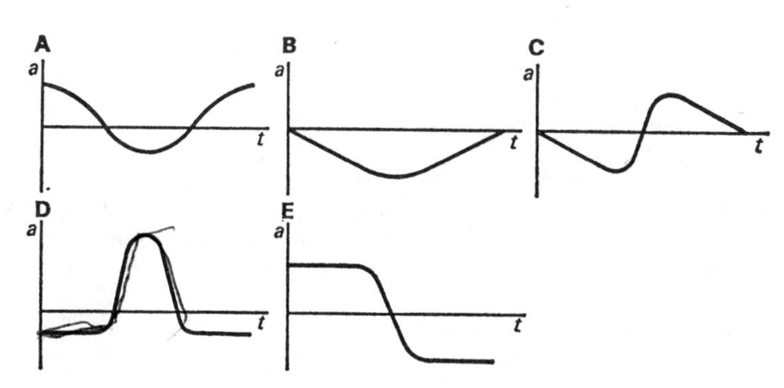

A8 In the previous question which graph shows the variation in the boy's vertical velocity, v, with time, t?

Newton's laws

A9 A golf ball of mass 0.05 kg is driven from the tee with a velocity of 70 m s^{-1}. If the period of contact with the clubhead was 5×10^{-4} s, the mean accelerating force on the ball was, to 2 significant figures

A 2.5×10^5 N **B** 7.0×10^3 N **C** 3.5×10^3 N **D** 1.4×10^3 N
E 1.2×10^2 N

A10 A particle is accelerated by a resultant force F. A graph of its acceleration, a, against F is shown. The mass of the particle is

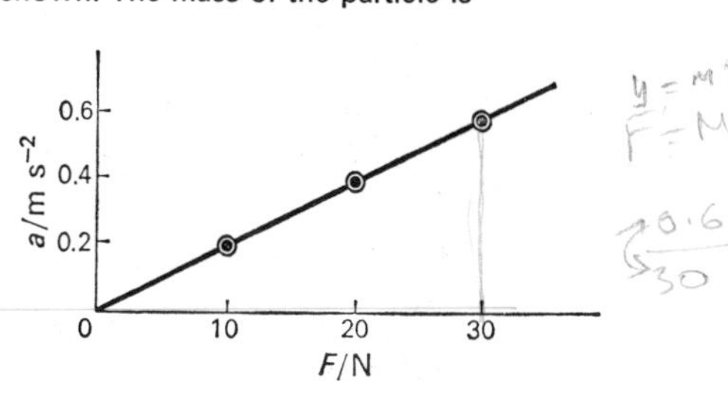

A 50 kg **B** 18 kg **C** 5 kg **D** 2 kg **E** 0.02 kg

A11 When a car accelerates horizontally along a straight road the accelerating force is

A the push of the air on the car
B the push of the car on the road
C the pull of the engine on the car
D the push of the rear axle on the wheels
E the push of the road on the car

A12 An unladen car moving with velocity u can be stopped in a distance s. If passengers add 40 per cent to its mass, and the braking force remains the same, the braking distance at velocity u is now

A $1.4\,s$ **B** $\sqrt{1.4}\,s$ **C** $(1.4)^2\,s$ **D** $1.2\,s$ **E** still s

A13 A man is standing in a lift which is moving down at a constant velocity. If the push of the floor on the man is P and the pull of the Earth on the man (his weight) is W, then the net force on the man is

A slightly greater than W, vertically downwards
B slightly greater than P, vertically upwards
C a fraction of P, vertically upwards
D a fraction of W, vertically downwards
E zero

A14 A box is accelerated upwards in a lift. The push of the box on the lift is equal in magnitude to the push of the lift on the box
BECAUSE
Newton's 3rd law applies to accelerating bodies

A15 A man stands on a lorry with a box as shown.

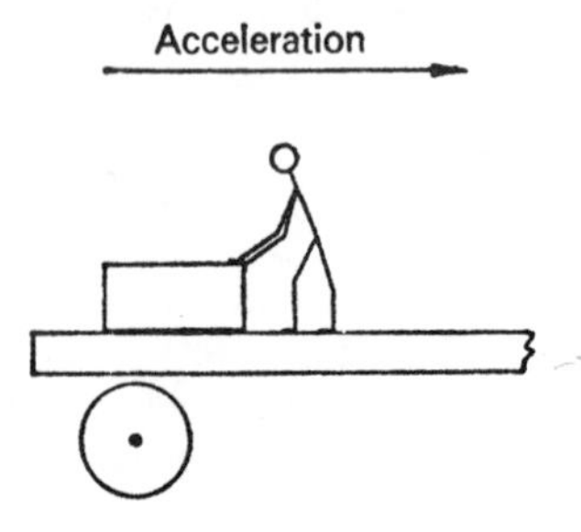

He exerts a force P, which could be a push or a pull, on the box. The lorry

accelerates to the right and the floor of the lorry is rough. Which of the following force diagrams shows a possible arrangement for the forces on the box?

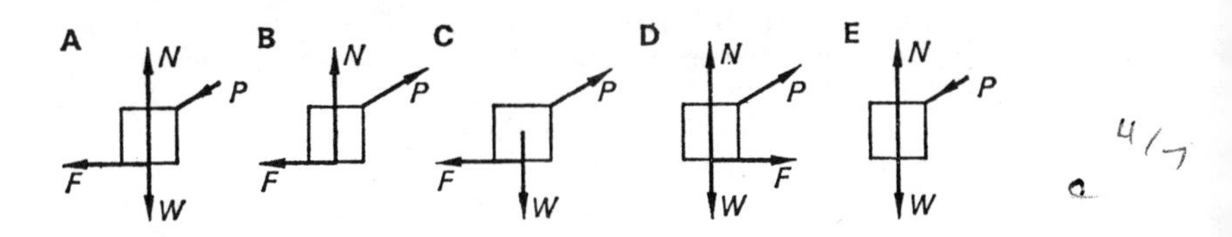

Warning—*in* **A16** *and* **A17** *you are given more information than you need.*

A16 A man is pulling a block of mass 4.0 kg along a frictionless table. At the instant shown the block is moving at 0.5 m s^{-1} and is accelerating at 1.0 m s^{-2}.

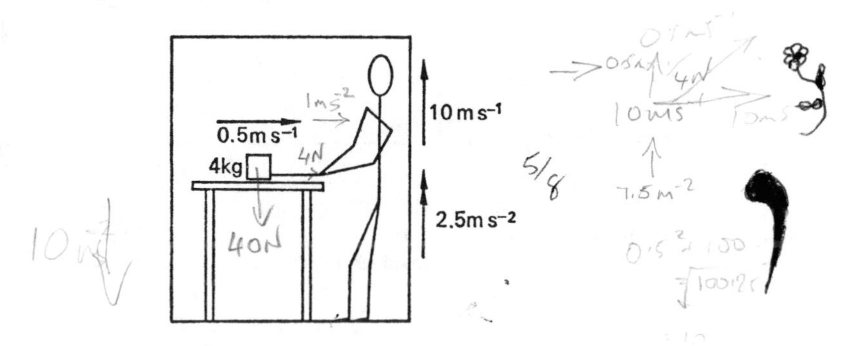

The operation is occurring in a lift moving upwards at 10 m s^{-1} and accelerating at 2.5 m s^{-2}. The pull of the man on the block is (take $g = 10$ N kg^{-1})

A zero **B** less than 8 N but not zero **C** 8 N **D** 10 N
E more than 10 N

A17 If, in the previous question, the table was not frictionless and there was a coefficient of sliding friction of 0.5, then the man would have to produce an extra pull on the block of (take $g = 10$ N kg^{-1})

A 4×0.5 N **B** 4×1.0 N **C** 4×2.5 N **D** 4×10 N
E $4 \times \frac{(10 + 2.5)}{2}$ N

A18 On the Moon the vertical acceleration of a body in free fall is about 1/6 of the corresponding figure on Earth. The invention of a less cumbersome space suit should lead, therefore, to new sporting records in the following events:

1 high jump **2** long jump **3** mass lifting **4** pole vault

A19 When a cycle is ridden at speed, the tension, T, in any one given spoke varies with time as shown in graph.
(N.B. The spokes support the load imposed on the hub of the wheel. You may assume that all spokes are at a tension T_0 when the cycle is lifted clear of the ground. The interval on each graph represents one revolution of the wheel.)

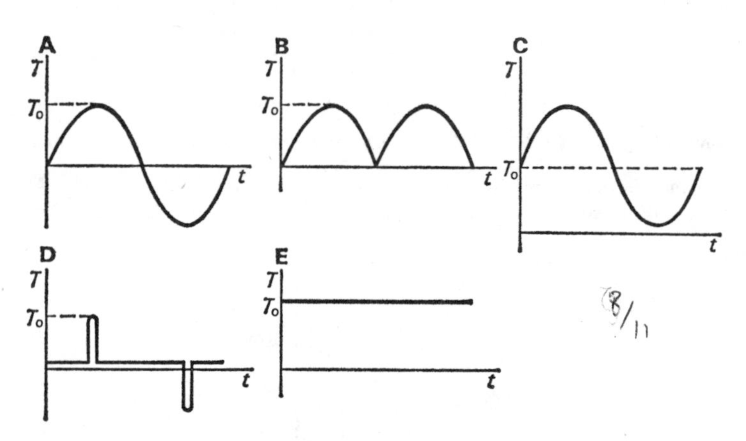

A20 A trolley of mass m accelerates from rest along a horizontal runway. The string, under tension F, passes over a pulley of circumference a. The pattern

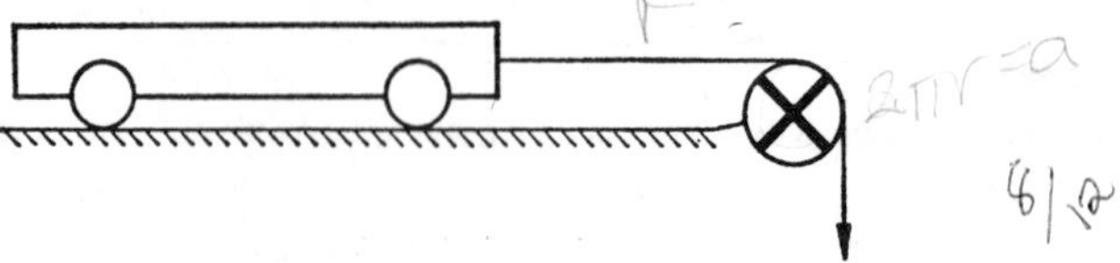

on the pulley, (a cross), is illuminated by a stroboscope flashing at a frequency n. The pattern first appears stationary after a time interval

A $\frac{anF}{4m}$ B $\frac{4nam}{F}$ C $\frac{aF}{4nm}$ D $\frac{nam}{4F}$ E $\frac{na}{4mF}$

A21 Two frictionless trolleys, P and Q, of mass 4 kg and 2 kg respectively are connected by a strong but light rubber band. They are pulled apart and released.

1 The acceleration of Q is twice that of P numerically
2 The trolleys will meet midway between their starting points
3 The pull of the rubber band on Q is numerically the same as the pull of the rubber band on P just after they are released
4 The velocity of P relative to Q is numerically twice the velocity of Q relative to P just before they meet

A22 A single horizontal force F is applied to the block of mass M, which is in contact with another block of mass m, and accelerates the blocks as shown.

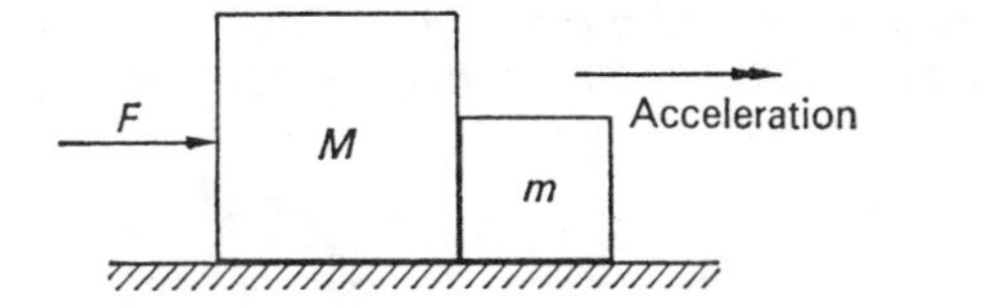

If the surfaces are frictionless and we ignore air resistance, then the size of the force between the blocks is

A $\frac{mF}{M+m}$ **B** $\frac{mF}{M}$ **C** $\frac{mF}{M-m}$ **D** $\frac{MF}{M+m}$ **E** $\frac{MF}{m}$

Statics

A23 A picture P of weight W is hung by two strings as shown from fixed points

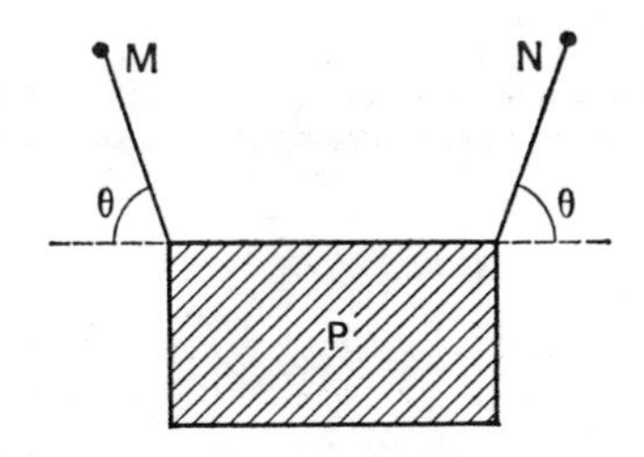

M and N. The tension in each string is T. The total upward pull of the strings on the picture is

A zero **B** $2W \cos\theta$ **C** $T \sin\theta$ **D** $T \cos\theta$ **E** $2T \sin\theta$

A24 The uniform plank, XY, is supported by initially equal forces of 120 N at X and Y. If the point of application of the force at X is now moved to Z (half-way to the centre) and the plank is still to be at rest and horizontal the force at Y must now be

120 N 120 N
X Z Y

A 240 N **B** still 120 N **C** 80 N **D** 60 N **E** 40 N

A25 A metal sphere is hung by a string fixed to a wall. The sphere is pushed away from the wall by a stick. The forces acting on the sphere are shown on the second diagram. Which of the following statements are true?

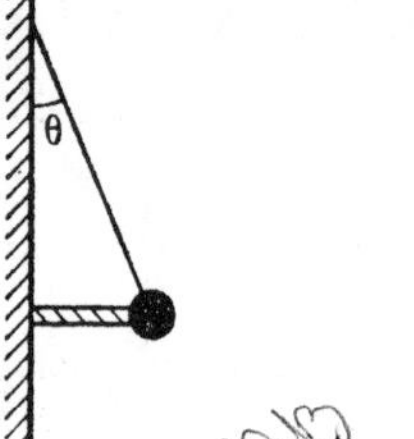

1 vector T + vector P + vector $W = 0$
2 $P = W \tan \theta$
3 $T^2 = P^2 + W^2$
4 $T = P + W$

A26 A person supports a book between finger and thumb as shown (the point of grip is assumed to be at the corner of the book). If the book has a weight of W then the person is producing a torque on the book of

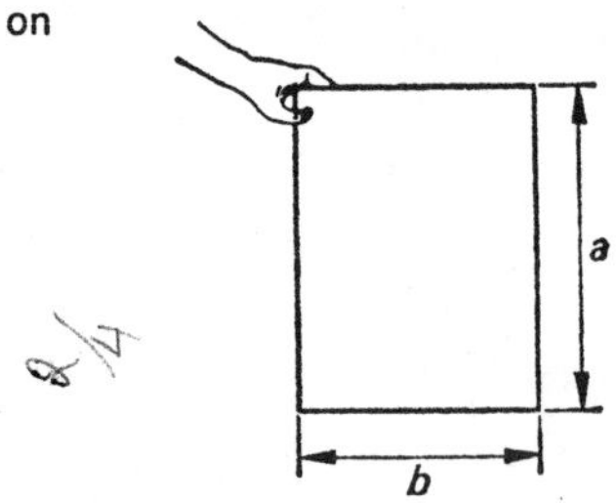

A $W\frac{a}{2}$ anticlockwise
B $W\frac{b}{2}$ anticlockwise
C Wa anticlockwise
D Wa clockwise
E Wb clockwise

A27 The diagram shows a uniform rectangular board PQRS, smoothly pivoted at its centre O. The board has a weight of 28 N. Two masses M and N are attached

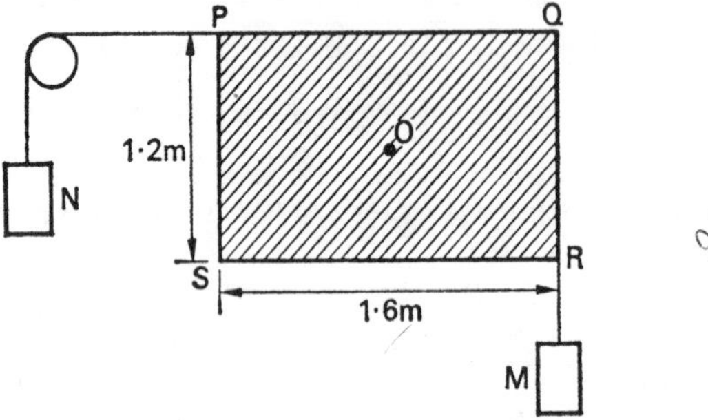

by light strings to the corners P and R as shown, the weight of M is 36 N. If the system is in equilibrium with the board in a vertical plane, the *size of* the push of the board on the rod supporting it at O is

A 28 N B 45 N C 60 N D 64 N E 80 N

Work and energy

A28 The energy required to raise a large volume of water from a reservoir to another reservoir higher up the mountain could be measured in

1 kilowatt hours **2** kilonewtons **3** megajoules **4** megawatts

A29 A motor using electrical energy at the rate of 400 W raises a block of weight 120 N. If the block moves 8.0 m vertically in 4.0 s, the efficiency of the motor is

A 24% **B** 30% **C** 48% **D** 60% **E** 96%

A30 A man (P) weighing 1000 N runs up a staircase in 12 s whereas man (Q) weighing 750 N takes 11 s to run up the same staircase. The ratio of the rates at which (P) and (Q) do work is

A 4:3 **B** 11:9 **C** 11:12 **D** 9:11 **E** 3:4

A31 A particle, initially at rest on a frictionless horizontal surface, is acted upon by a horizontal force which is constant in size and direction. A graph is plotted of the work done on the particle, W, against the speed of the particle, v. If there are no other horizontal forces acting on the particle the graph would look like

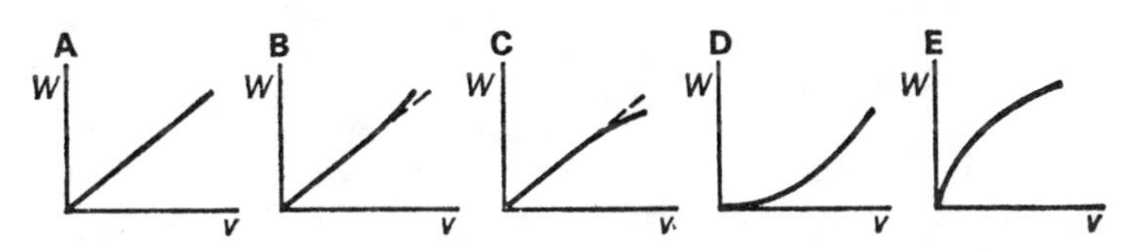

A32 A force acting on a particle does work on it. If the particle moves along a line parallel to the force and the relation between the force and the distance is as shown then the work done is, to 1 significant figure,

A 2 J **B** 4 J **C** 8 J **D** 20 J **E** 30 J

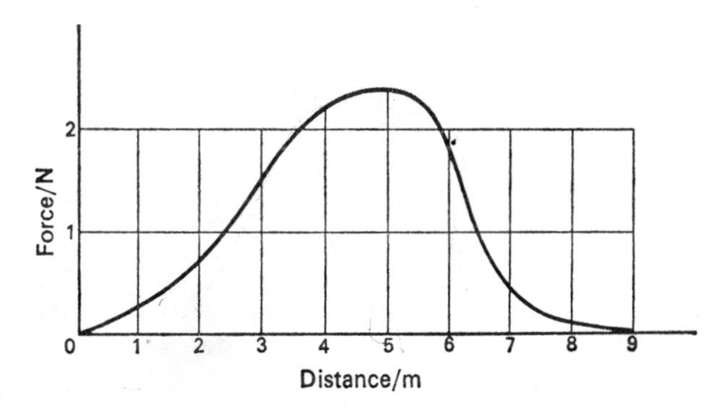

A33 A dynamics trolley has a piston and spring attachment. It is pushed up against a wall as shown and held at rest. It is then released and its motion is indicated in the diagram.

The push of the wall on the piston of the trolley does no work.

BECAUSE

it does not move its point of application.

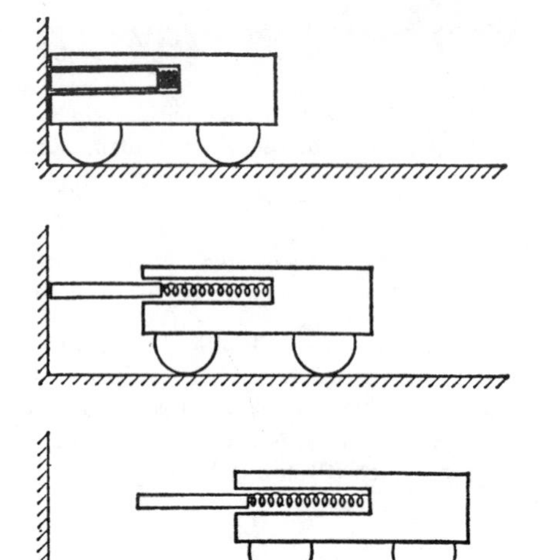

A34 A light elastic cord of natural length OA is fixed at O and loaded with a mass m which then oscillates between A and C. The elastic energy stored instantaneously in the cord when it is fully stretched at C is

A $mgh/4$ **B** $mgh/2$ **C** $mgh/\sqrt{2}$
D mgh **E** $2mgh$

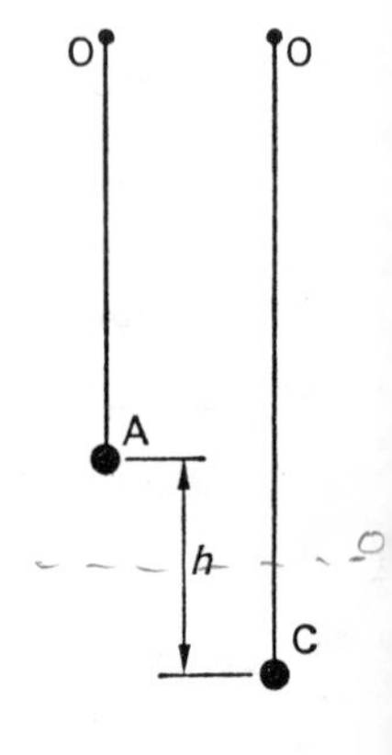

A35 A cricket ball is hit for six, leaving the bat at an angle of 45° to the horizontal with kinetic energy K. At the top of its flight its kinetic energy is (neglecting air resistance)

A zero **B** $K/4$ **C** $K/2$ **D** $K/\sqrt{2}$ **E** still K

A36 A body falls from rest freely under gravity. If its speed is v when it has lost an amount V of gravitational potential energy, then the mass of the body is

A $\frac{v^2}{2g}$ **B** $\frac{Vg}{v^2}$ **C** $\frac{V}{g}$ **D** $\frac{2V}{v^2}$ **E** $2Vgv^2$

A37 The graph shows how the potential energy, V, of a particle varies with its distance, x, from a fixed point. A graph showing how the force, F, on the particle varies with x would look like

A

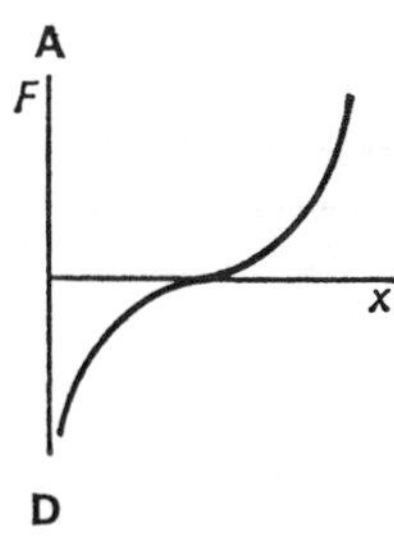

B

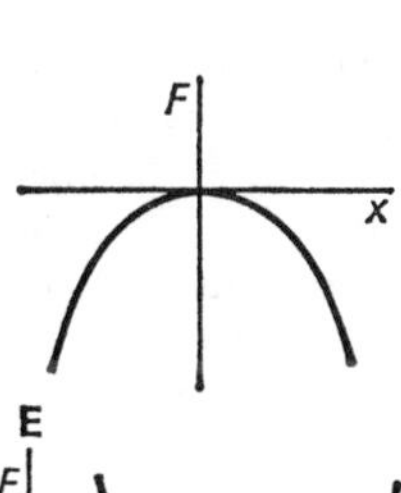

C

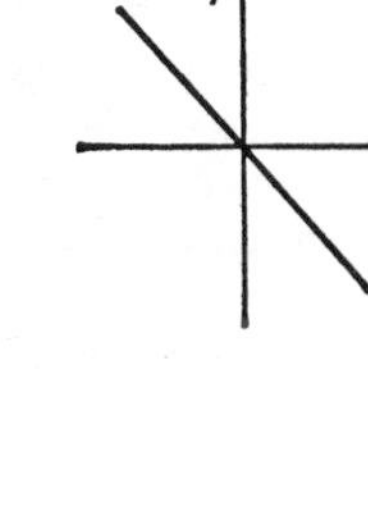

D

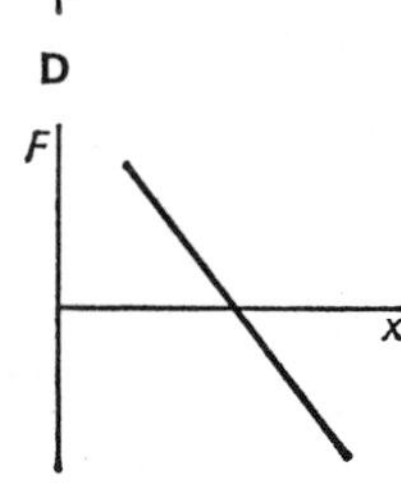

E

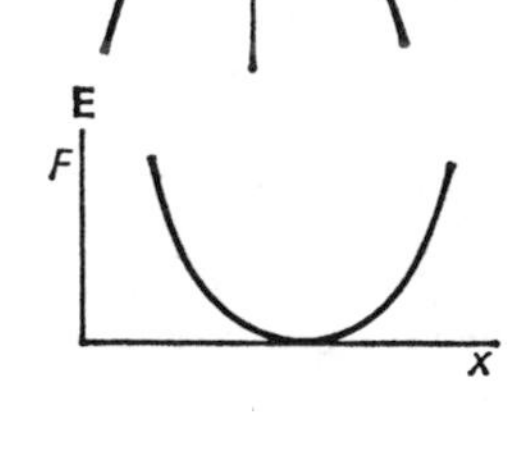

Circular motion

A38 When moving in a circle at a constant speed a particle of fixed mass

1 undergoes zero displacement in making one complete revolution
2 is moving with a continuously changing velocity
3 is subject to a centripetal force
4 has a constant kinetic energy

A39 The bicycle in the diagram is being ridden to the left at a steady speed. Points at X and Y on the wheels will have, at the instant shown, velocities relative to the ground in the following directions

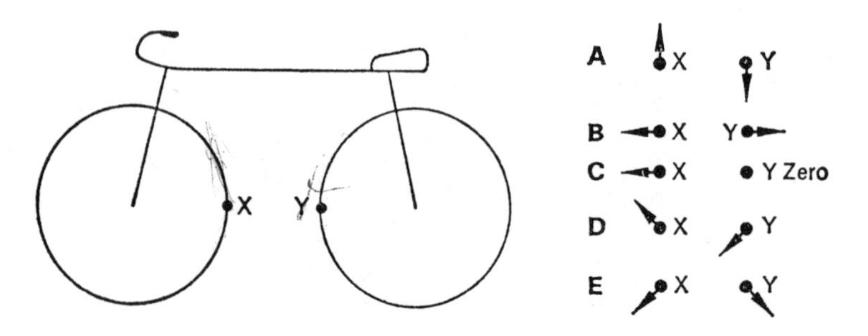

A40 A car travels north with uniform velocity. It goes over a piece of mud, which sticks to the tyre. The initial acceleration of the mud, as it leaves the ground, is

A vertically upwards
B horizontally to the north
C horizontally to the south
D zero
E upwards and forwards, at 45° to the horizontal

A41 A particle is moving in a circle of radius r with constant speed v. The size of the *change* in velocity between P and Q is

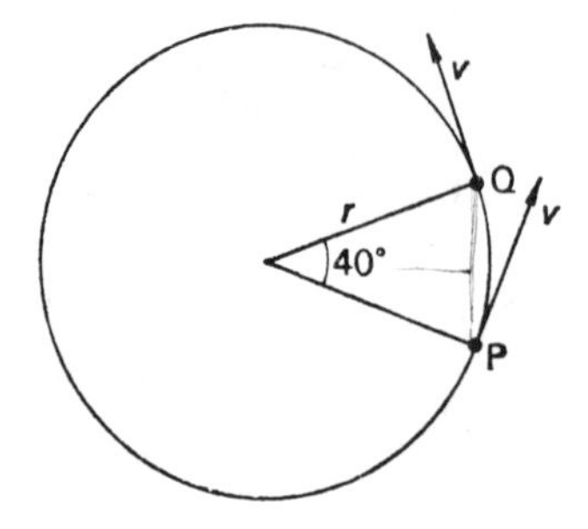

A zero
B $v \sin 40°$
C $2v \sin 20°$
D $v \cos 20°$
E v

A42 The string of a simple pendulum which is swinging through an arc in a vertical plane is most likely to break when the bob is directly underneath the point of suspension
BECAUSE
the pull of the Earth on the pendulum bob and the pull of the string on the pendulum bob are then equal in magnitude

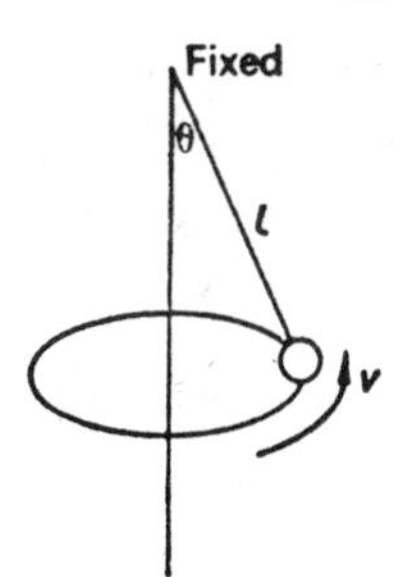

A43 A metal sphere is suspended from a light thread of length l and is whirled in a horizontal circle at a constant speed v.
The forces on the sphere, as described by an observer who is at rest, are shown in diagram

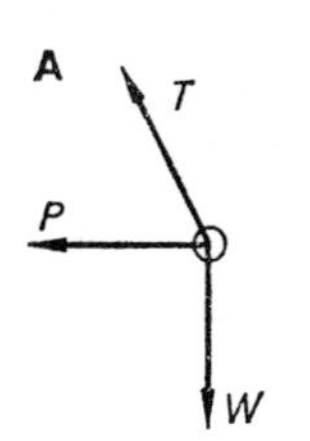

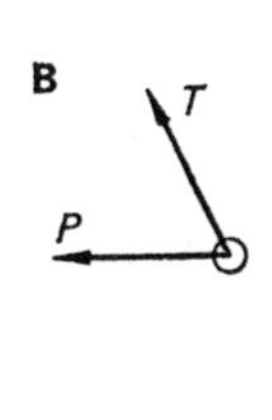

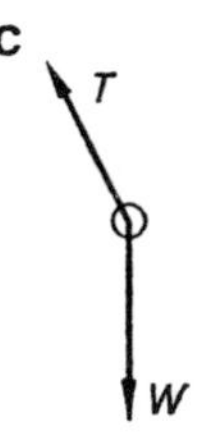

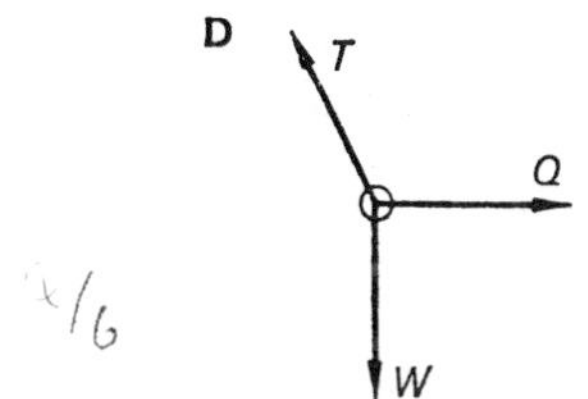

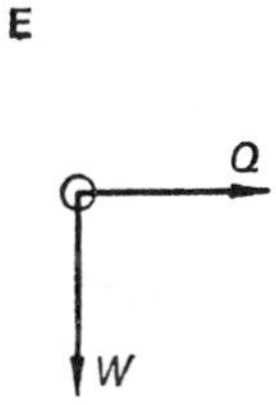

A44 The time taken for the sphere described in question **A43** above to complete one revolution is

A $\dfrac{v^2}{l \sin\theta}$ **B** $v^2 / l \sin\theta$ **C** $2\pi l v \cos\theta$ **D** $\dfrac{2\pi l \sin\theta}{v}$ **E** $\dfrac{2\pi l}{v}$

A45 Given values for l, v, and θ, in **A43**, one may calculate (besides the time for one revolution)

A the mass of the sphere
B the weight of the sphere
C the mass and the weight of the sphere
D g
E the mass and the weight of the sphere and g

A46 A toy car travels in a horizontal circle of radius $2a$, kept on track by a radial elastic string of unstretched length a. The period of rotation is T. When the car is speeded up the string stretches until the car is moving in a circle of radius $3a$. Assuming that the string obeys Hooke's law, the period of rotation is now

A unaltered **B** $\frac{3}{4}T$ **C** $\sqrt{\frac{3}{4}}\,T$ **D** $\frac{3^2}{4^2}T$ **E** $\sqrt{\frac{4}{3}}\,T$

A47 The model horse on a merry-go-round does work on a child seated firmly on it which is equal to $2\left(\frac{mv^2}{r} \times 2r\right)$ per revolution

BECAUSE

the horizontal force, $\frac{mv^2}{r}$, acting on the child is reversed in direction twice in each revolution. (m = mass of child
r = radius of revolution
v = steady speed of child).

A48 A uniform solid metal bar AOB spins at a steady rate about a central pivot, O. The resulting longitudinal strain set up in it increases from the centre O, to the two ends A and B

BECAUSE

the centripetal force needed per unit length of the bar is greatest at A and B.

Linear momentum

A49 A ball of mass 1.0 kg moving at 2.0 m s^{-1} perpendicularly towards a wall rebounds with a speed of 1.5 m s^{-1}. The gain of momentum of the ball is

A zero **B** 0.5 N s away from the wall **C** 0.5 N s towards the wall
D 3.5 N s away from the wall **E** 3.5 N s towards the wall

A50 The momentum acquired by a body of mass 5 kg acted on by the force which varies in a manner described by the graph is

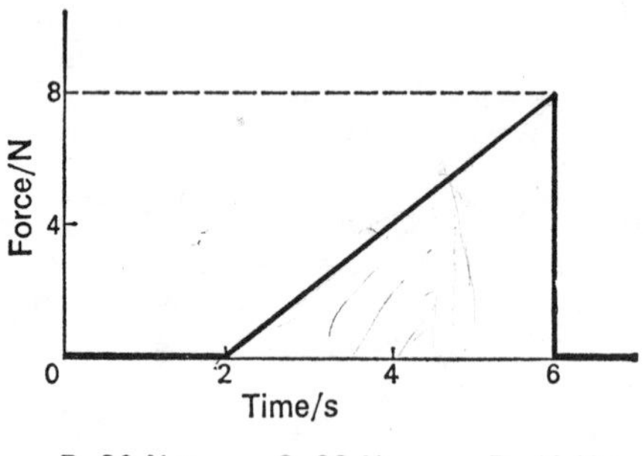

A 16 N s **B** 30 N s **C** 32 N s **D** 40 N s **E** 48 N s

A51 A golf ball of mass m on a tee is hit by a club so that it leaves the tee at a speed v. The club is in contact with the ball for a short time interval Δt. The average push of the club on the ball is

A $mv\Delta t$ **B** $\frac{mv}{\Delta t}$ **C** $\frac{1}{2}mv^2\Delta t$ **D** $\frac{mv^2}{2\Delta t}$ **E** $\frac{m(\Delta t)^2}{2v}$

A52 In a perfectly elastic collision between two air-supported pucks there is no net loss of linear momentum
BECAUSE
the work done in slowing one down is exactly equal to the work done in speeding the other one up.

A53 The figure shows a graph on which the velocities of two vehicles moving in the same straight line are represented. The vehicles collide after 3 s. If the vehicles are denoted by suffixes 1 and 2 so that they have masses m_1 and m_2, then

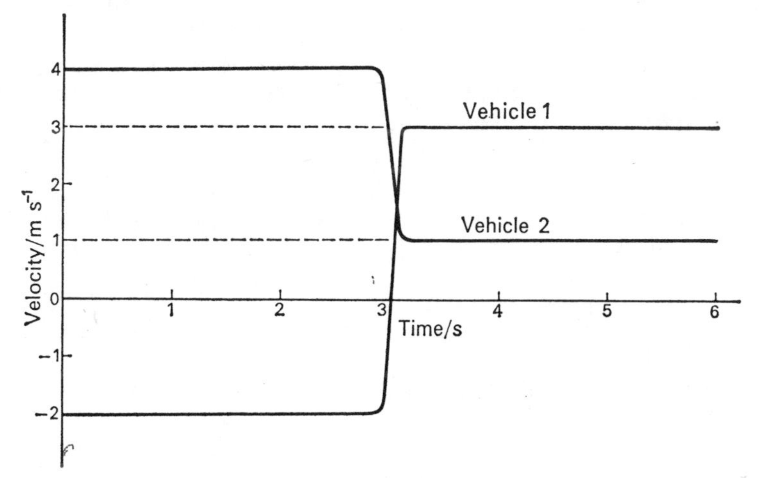

A $m_1 = 3m_2$ **B** $3m_1 = m_2$ **C** $3m_1 = 5m_2$ **D** $3m_1 = 7m_2$ **E** $5m_1 = 3m_2$

A54 A rocket engine is mounted on a railway wagon which is free to move along a horizontal track. The acceleration of the wagon when the engine is first ignited does *not* depend upon

1 the mass of exhaust gas emitted per second
2 the mass of the railway wagon
3 the velocity of the exhaust gases relative to the nozzle of the rocket
4 the local value of g

A55 A stream of water in a horizontal jet strikes a rigid wall and is brought to rest before falling vertically. In order to calculate the force on the wall caused by the water we must

1 calculate the rate of loss of kinetic energy of the water
2 calculate the rate of change of momentum of the water
3 use the principle of conservation of energy
4 use Newton's 2nd law in the form force is proportional to the rate of change of momentum

A56 Steady rain, giving 5 mm an hour, turns suddenly into a downpour giving 20 mm an hour, and the speed of the raindrops falling vertically on to a flat roof simultaneously doubles. The pressure exerted by the falling rain on the roof rises by a factor of

A 2 **B** $2\sqrt{2}$ **C** 4 **D** $4\sqrt{2}$ **E** 8

A57 A fat hosepipe is held horizontal by a fireman. It delivers water through a constricting nozzle at one litre per second. On increasing the pressure, this increases to two litres per second. The fireman now has to

A push forward, four times as hard
B push forward, twice as hard
C pull backwards, twice as hard
D pull backwards, four times as hard
E push forward, $\sqrt{2}$ times as hard

A58 A man stands on an open truck which can run on frictionless horizontal rails as shown. The man and the truck are at rest. The man now walks to the other end of the truck and stops.

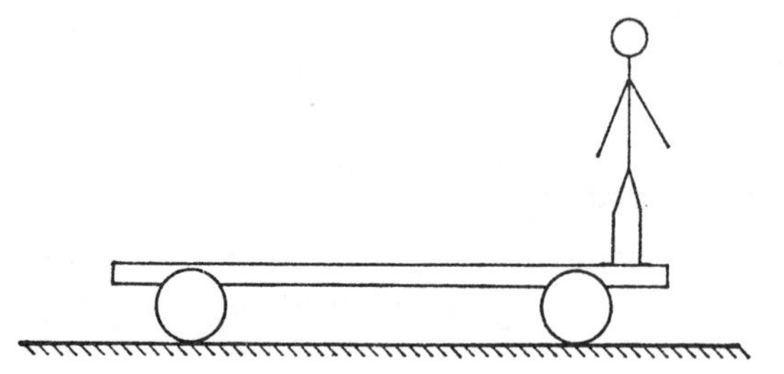

1 The truck continues to move to the right after the man ceases to walk along it
2 The centre of mass of the (man plus truck) remains at rest throughout the man's walk
3 The kinetic energy of the man is at all times equal to that of the truck during the man's walk
4 The push of the man on the truck is equal in size to the push of the truck on the man at all times during the man's walk

A59 The diagram represents five photographs showing two-dimensional collisions between a moving nucleus, entering at left, and a stationary nucleus in a bubble chamber. The length of the tracks shown are of no significance but their relative directions are. Which photograph, assuming there were no other particles involved in the collision, shows an impossible situation?

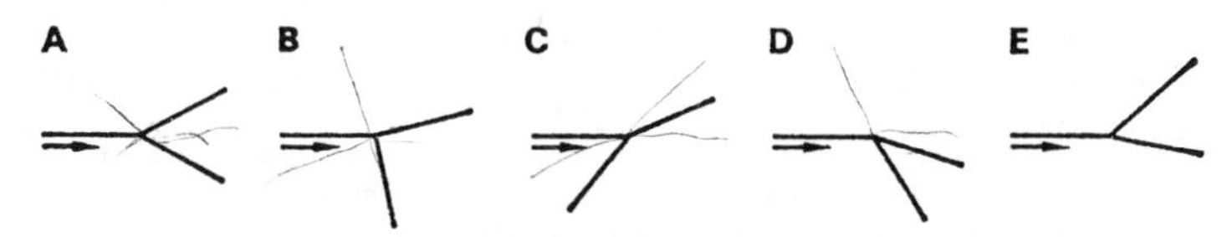

A60 In which of the photographs represented in question **A59** is it possible to deduce which track *after* the collision is that of the nucleus which was originally at rest?

A61 Suppose the bombarding nucleus shown entering at left in the diagrams of question **A59** was a helium nucleus $^4_2$He. In which photograph *must* the nucleus it hit have also been a helium nucleus?

Mechanical oscillations

A62 Here is a list of things involving oscillations:

p—a simple pendulum 0.4 m long
q—a musical note near the bottom (low pitch) end of a piano
r—a wrist watch balance wheel
s—a rope suspension bridge 30 m long

Which of the following correctly places them in order of *increasing* frequency:

A p q r s **B** q s p r **C** r p s q **D** s p r q **E** s r q p

A63 The velocity and acceleration of a particle performing simple harmonic motion have a steady phase relationship. The acceleration shows a phase lead over the velocity, in radians of,

A plus π **B** plus $\pi/2$ **C** zero **D** minus $\pi/2$ **E** minus π

A64 Two points F and G perform simple harmonic motion along the same straight line, with the same amplitude, s_0, and the same frequency, f. The greatest distance between F and G noticed by an observer studying the motion is found to be s_0. Hence we can deduce that in this case F leads G (or G leads F) by a phase angle of

A π **B** $2\pi/3$ **C** $\pi/2$ **D** $\pi/3$ **E** $\pi/6$

A65 In question **A64**, points F and G will coincide momentarily when their displacement is plus or minus

A s_0 **B** $\frac{\sqrt{3}s_0}{2}$ **C** $\frac{s_0}{\sqrt{2}}$ **D** $\frac{s_0}{2}$ **E** $\frac{\sqrt{3}s_0}{2\sqrt{2}}$

A66 A body rests on a frictionless horizontal surface. It is attached to a horizontal spring and oscillates with simple harmonic motion in a straight line about a point. If displacements etc. are measured relative to this point, then which of the following ratios are constant?

1 displacement/acceleration
2 displacement/period
3 displacement/pull(or push) of spring on body
4 velocity/displacement

A67 A body performs simple harmonic motion along the straight line MNOPQ.

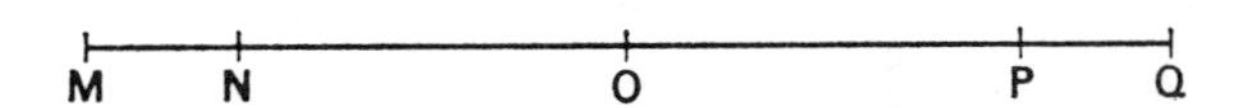

Its kinetic energy at N, and at P, is one half of its peak value at O. If the period of oscillation is T then the time taken to travel from N to P directly, along NOP, is

A $\frac{1}{2}T$ **B** $\frac{1}{4}T$ **C** $T/2\sqrt{2}$ **D** $T/8$ **E** $T/4\sqrt{2}$

A68 A trolley, T, can run on a frictionless table. Two much smaller but equal masses, P and Q, are hung by strings which pass over frictionless pulleys as shown. The string is of such a length that when T is in equilibrium, P and Q both just

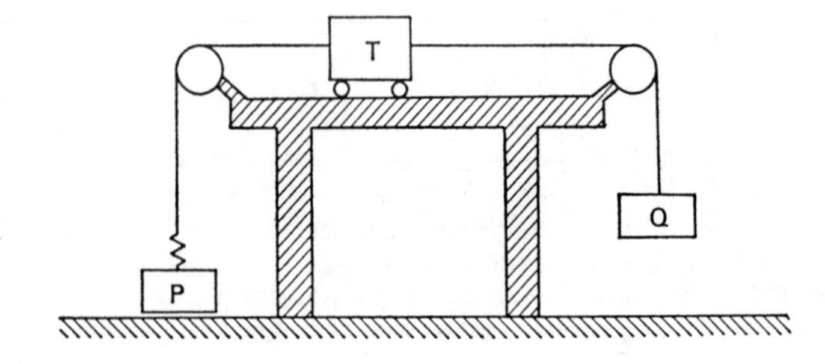

touch the ground. T is pulled to one side and released. A graph of the velocity, v, of the trolley against time, t, would look like

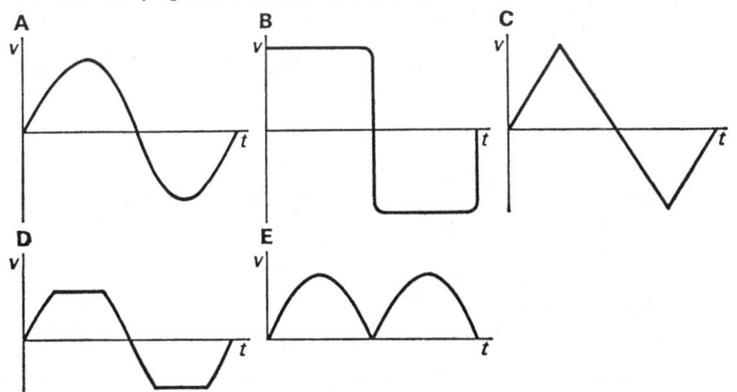

A69 A small massive trolley oscillates about Q. On one side it runs up a slight uniform incline to R, and on the other side it compresses a helical spring to P. PQ

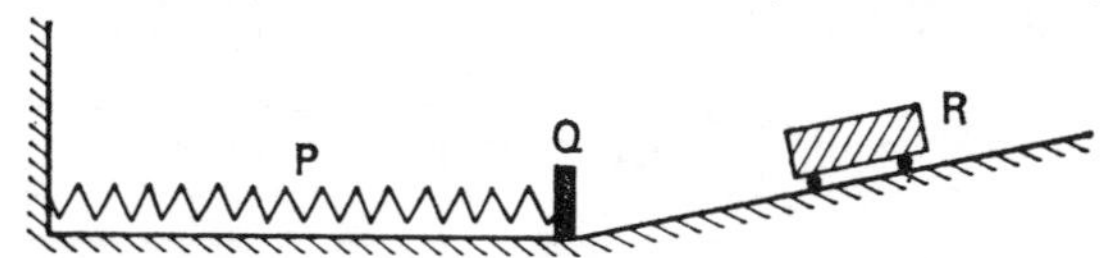

is approximately equal to QR. Assume that there is no loss of mechanical energy during the oscillation. The trolley executes simple harmonic motion about Q
BECAUSE
its acceleration is always directed towards Q.

A70 Which of the graphs shows the variation of the horizontal velocity, v, of the trolley in question **A69** with time, t?

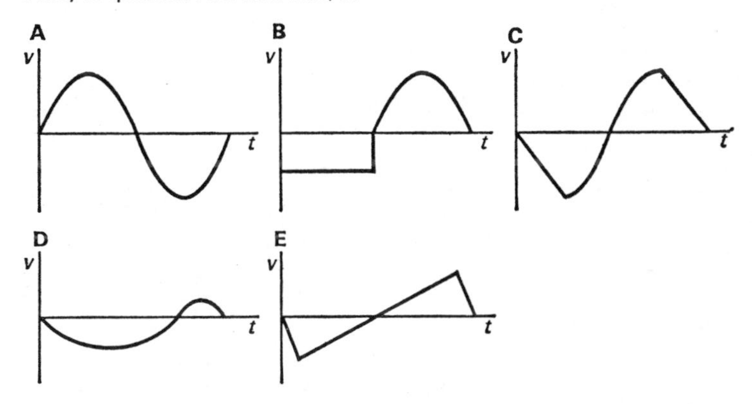

A71 Which graph shape above (question **A70**) could show the variation of the acceleration, a, of the trolley in question **A69** with time, t?

A72 If the motion of the trolley described in question **A69** *did* dissipate mechanical energy so that the motion slowly dies away, then the trolley would spend more and more of its *time* in the section PQ
BECAUSE
the mean restoring force there is decreasing while that in section QR remains unchanged.

A73 A body performs simple harmonic motion. Its kinetic energy, T, varies with time, t, as indicated in graph

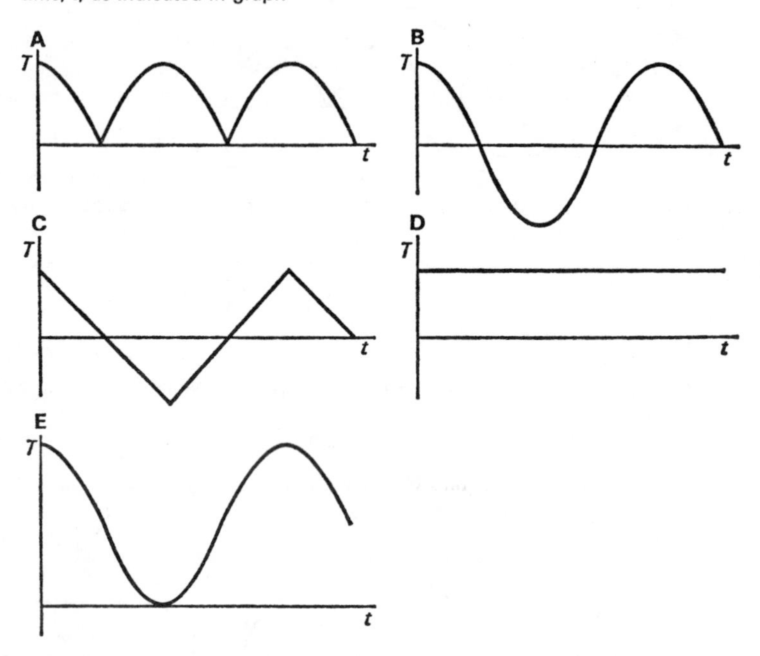

A74 A trolley is attached to two fixed walls by identical light springs. It is set to oscillate with simple harmonic motion, (ignore resistance forces) and as it oscillates its kinetic energy, T, varies as does the elastic potential energy, V, stored in the springs.

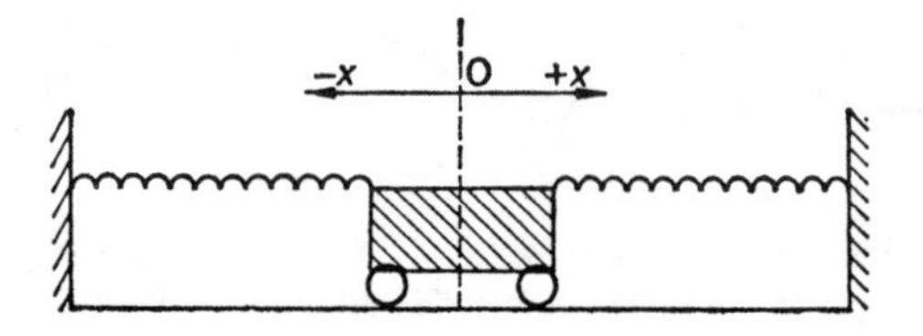

If the distance of the trolley from the central equilibrium position is x, the following energy–distance relations are true

1

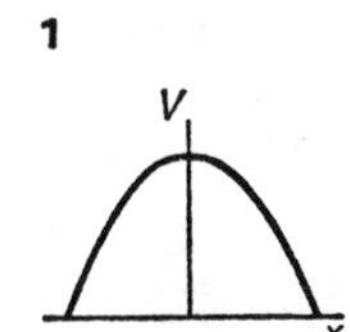

2

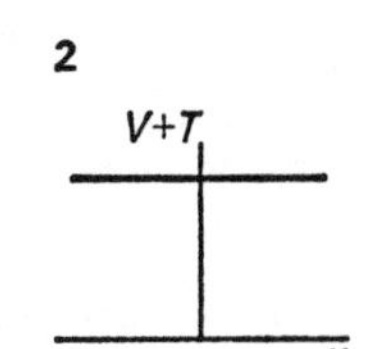

3

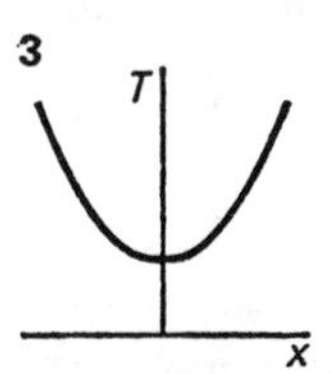

4

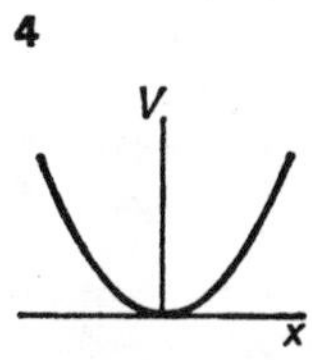

A75 Two simple pendulums with lengths 1 m and 16 m are both given small displacements in the same direction at the same time. They will next be in phase after the shorter pendulum has completed n oscillations, where n is

A $\frac{1}{4}$ **B** $1\frac{1}{3}$ **C** 4 **D** 5 **E** 16

A76 Two light, identical, helical springs, PQ, ST, of natural length b, are hung vertically at fixed points P and S and loaded with masses m and $2m$ respectively. On release these perform simple harmonic motion from Q to X, and from T to Y. Then the ratio $\frac{\text{acceleration at X}}{\text{acceleration at Y}}$ is

A $\frac{1}{4}$ **B** $\frac{1}{2}$ **C** 1 **D** 2 **E** 4

A77 A heavy brass sphere is hung from a spiral spring and executes vertical oscillations with period T. The ball is now immersed in a *non-viscous* liquid with a density one tenth that of brass. When it is set in vertical oscillation, its period is

A unchanged **B** $\frac{9^2}{10^2}T$ **C** $\frac{10^2}{9^2}T$

D $\frac{9}{10}T$ **E** $\sqrt{\frac{9}{10}}T$

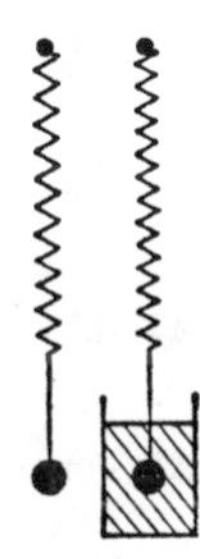

A78 A heavy brass sphere is hung on a cord and as a simple pendulum it has a period T.

When it is now immersed in a *non-viscous* liquid of density one tenth that of brass, its period is

A unchanged **B** $\frac{9}{10}T$ **C** $\frac{10^2}{9^2}T$ **D** $\sqrt{\frac{10}{9}}T$ **E** $\frac{10}{9}T$

A79 A simple pendulum is made to oscillate by imposing a small horizontal simple harmonic motion on its point of support. As the frequency of the drive rises from zero to the point at which resonance occurs, the phase lead of the support over the pendulum bob

A decreases from zero to $-\pi/2$
B increases from $-\pi/2$ to $+\pi/2$
C increases from zero to $+\pi/2$
D increases from $-\pi/2$ to zero
E decreases from $+\pi/2$ to zero

A80 When a mechanical system is in resonance

1 the driving force is in phase with the displacement
2 the power transfer from the source to the system is a maximum for that driving force
3 the forces damping the oscillation are at a minimum value
4 the driving frequency is the same as the natural frequency of the system

A81 A ripple tank vibrator produces water waves such that the displacement y of a particle in the water surface is given at time t by

$$y = y_0 \sin k(x - vt)$$

1 the amplitude of the wave is y_0
2 the wave is travelling in the negative x-direction
3 the wavelength of the wave is $2\pi/k$
4 the speed of the wave is kv

Further mechanics

A82 On account of the Earth's rotation on its axis a plumb-line in the latitude of Britain does not point directly towards the Earth's centre, but is deflected slightly to the

A north **B** south **C** south-east **D** south-west **E** west

A83 A solid cylinder, S, and a tube, T, of equal mass and the same external diameter each have a cotton thread wrapped around them one end of which is held firmly to the circumference and the other end fixed to a rigid horizontal support. If they are released together in the position shown in the figure then S reaches the floor before T

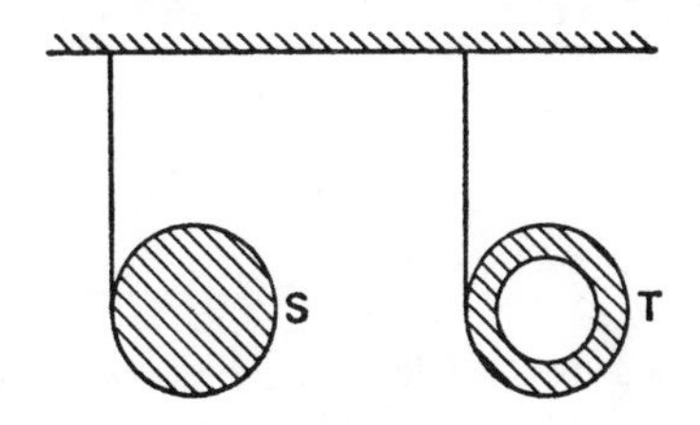

BECAUSE

S will then have a greater kinetic energy than T.

A84 A uniform heavy disc is rotating at constant angular velocity about a vertical axis through its centre and perpendicular to the plane of the disc. A lump of plasticine is dropped vertically on to the disc and sticks to it.

The angular velocity of the disc does not change

BECAUSE

the angular momentum of the system about the axis of rotation after impact is the same as before the impact. (N.B. system = disc + plasticine)

A85 Two heavy point masses, G and K, each of mass m, are joined by a stiff light rod, GHK, where $GK = 4\,GH$. The period of small oscillations from side to side is found to be T_1 when suspended at G, and T_2 when suspended at H.

The ratio T_1/T_2 is

A $\sqrt{3}$ **B** $\sqrt{4}$ **C** $\sqrt{8/5}$

D 1 **E** $\sqrt{4/5}$

A86 A circular wire ring, of mass m and radius r, hangs over a horizontal peg and performs small oscillations from side to side as shown. The period of the oscillation is

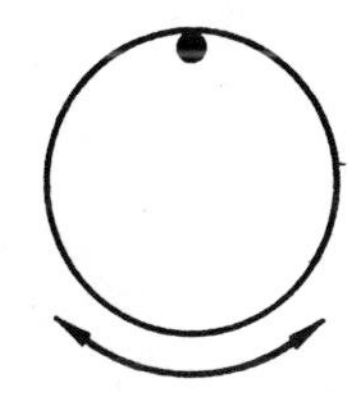

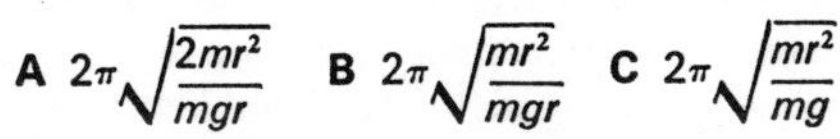

A $2\pi\sqrt{\dfrac{2mr^2}{mgr}}$ **B** $2\pi\sqrt{\dfrac{mr^2}{mgr}}$ **C** $2\pi\sqrt{\dfrac{mr^2}{mg}}$

D $2\pi\sqrt{\dfrac{2mr^2}{mg}}$ **E** $2\pi\sqrt{\dfrac{2mgr}{3mr^2}}$

B MECHANICAL PROPERTIES OF MATTER

Hydrostatics

B1 Each of the vessels shown is filled to a depth h with liquid of density ρ. The downward thrust of the liquid on the base of each vessel is different

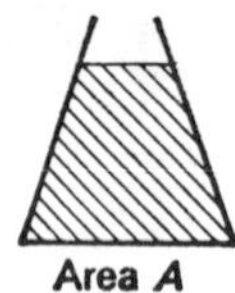

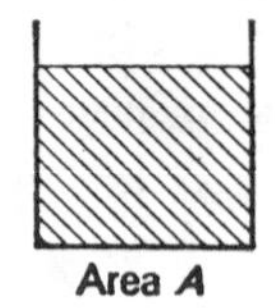

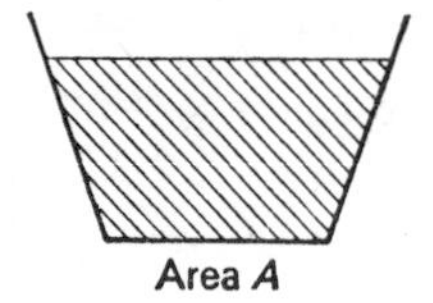

BECAUSE
the weight of the liquid is different in each of the vessels.

B2 The domestic gas pressure at the bottom of a hill is greater than that at the top of the hill
BECAUSE
air is denser than domestic gas.
(*Note*: Consider the *absolute* and not the *differential* gas pressure)

B3 A U-tube manometer is made by connecting two wide tubes by a piece of plastic hose. One side of the manometer is connected to the gas supply and the other side is open to the atmosphere. The difference in vertical height between the two liquid surfaces depends upon

1 the diameter of the pipe connecting the two tubes
2 the ratio of the diameters of the two tubes
3 the orientation of the two tubes, e.g. the angle between them
4 the density of the liquid in the manometer

B4 A tube of length h, which is wide enough to make surface tension effects negligible, is closed at one end. It is then lowered into a tank of mercury of depth h and the mercury rises a distance x into the tube. If the mercury barometer stands at h also then

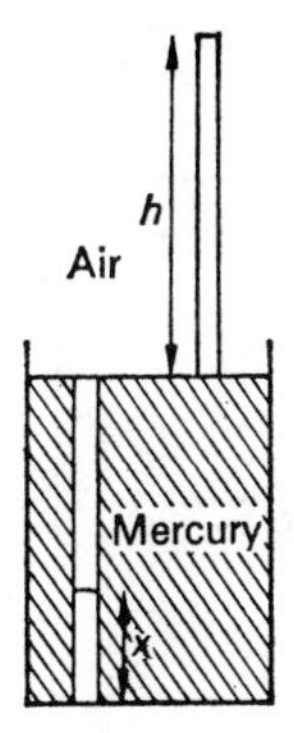

A $(2h - x)(h - x) = h^2$ **B** $(2h - x)(h + x) = h^2$
C $h(h - x) = h^2$ **D** $2h(h - x) = h^2$
E $(h - x)(2h + x) = h^2$

B5 A simple U-tube experiment is set up as illustrated. Both the oil and the petrol are less dense than water. Overnight evaporation of the *petrol* causes the free *oil* level to drop a short distance x. The free petrol surface has therefore

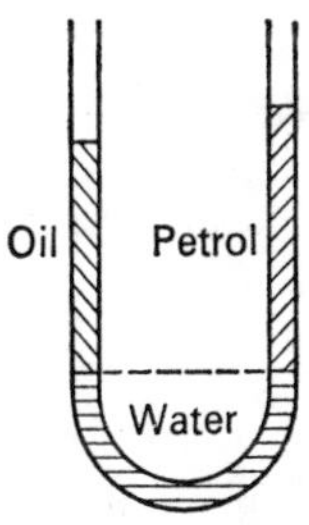

A risen a distance more than x **B** risen a distance less than x
C remained stationary **D** fallen a distance less than x
E fallen a distance more than x

B6 A mercury barometer, set up in a sealed cabin on the Moon containing air at our usual atmospheric pressure and temperature would stand at about

A 760 mm **B** 760/6 mm **C** 6×760 mm **D** zero
E a height dictated by the height of the roof of the cabin

(*Note:* g on the Moon is about one sixth of its value on Earth)

B7 A liquid of density ρ is pumped by a pump at P from situation (i) to situation (ii)

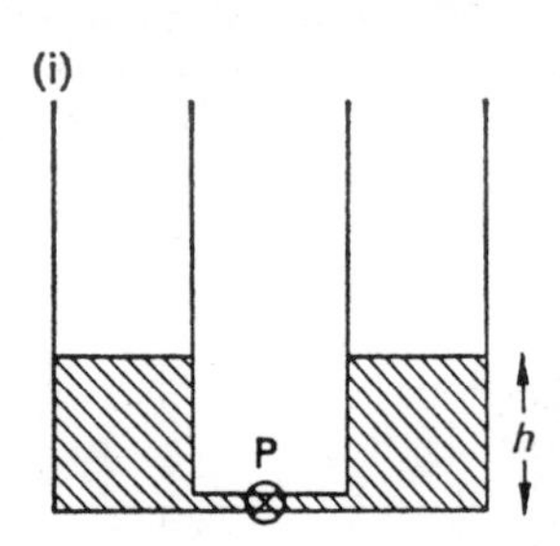

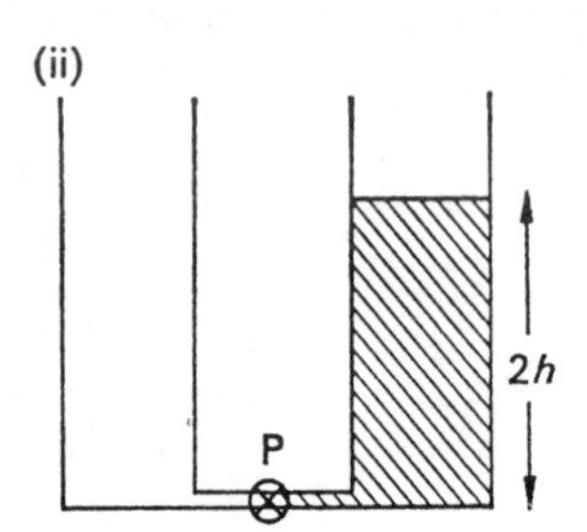

as shown in the diagram. If the cross-section of each of the vessels is A then the work done in pumping (ignore all friction effects) is

A $2\rho gh$ **B** ρgAh **C** $2\rho gAh$ **D** ρgAh^2 **E** $2\rho gAh^2$

B8 An object hangs from a spring balance. The balance registers 30 N in air, 20 N when this object is immersed in water and 24 N when the object is immersed in another liquid of unknown density. If the density of water is ρ, the density of the liquid is

A $\frac{30-20}{24-20}\rho$ **B** $\frac{30-24}{30-20}\rho$ **C** $\frac{24}{20}\rho$ **D** $\frac{24-20}{30-20}\rho$ **E** $\frac{30-20}{30}\rho$

B9 A body floating in equilibrium is acted on by two forces, the pull of the Earth on it, W, and the push of the liquid on it, U.

1 U acts through the centre of mass of the floating body
2 W and U act in the same vertical line
3 The size of U is dependent upon the density of the liquid in which the body is floating
4 W must equal U in size

B10 The scale on a (constant mass) hydrometer

1 will be longer for a given range of densities if the cross-sectional area of the stem is made narrower
2 is not linear
3 has the high density readings at the bottom of the stem when it is floating upright in a liquid
4 would need recalibrating for use on the Moon

B11 The mass of a block of glass of density ρ is found using known masses made of brass and a beam balance. The density of brass is 3ρ. The glass is reckoned to have mass M. The true mass of the glass, the mass it would be reckoned to have if the experiment were done in a vacuum, is M', where

A $M' = M$ **B** M' is 3 per cent greater than M
C M' is 2 per cent greater than M **D** $M' < M$
E there is no deducible relationship between M' and M

B12 A block of wood (of density 800 kg m^{-3}) floats in a freshwater lake (of density 1000 kg m^{-3}). Its dimensions are 1 m × 1 m × 0·1 m. It is pushed down slowly into the liquid until it is just submerged. Assume that the level of the lake does not rise appreciably during the immersion of the block. The work done to push the block under is (take $g = 10$ N kg^{-1})

A 2 J **B** 8 J **C** 10 J **D** 18 J **E** 80 J

B13 The diagram shows a small beaker containing lead shot floating in water in a large beaker. When the lead shot is poured from the small beaker into the

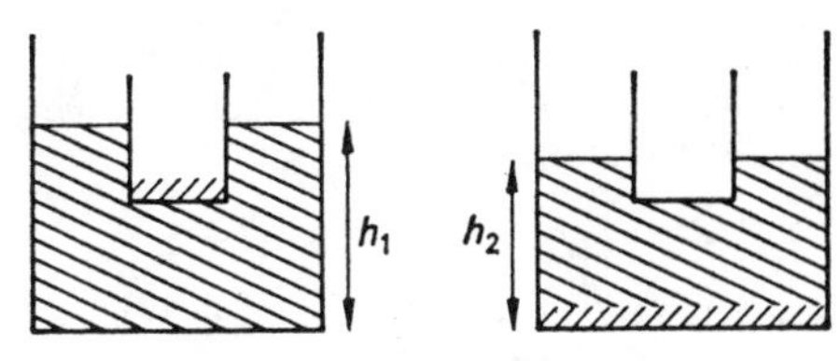

water and the small beaker is replaced floating in the water as shown in the second diagram, the height h_1 of the water *falls* to h_2
BECAUSE
the lead shot displaces its own volume of water in each case.

Surface tension

B14 Liquid reaches an equilibrium as shown in a capillary tube of internal radius r.

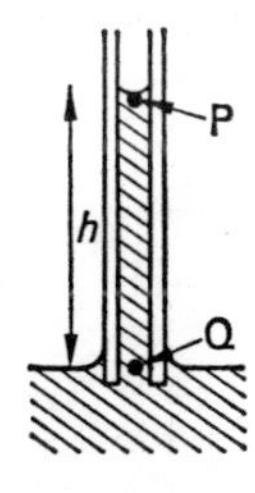

If the surface tension of the liquid is γ, the angle of contact θ, and the density of the liquid ρ, then the pressure difference ρgh between P and Q is equal to

A $\frac{2\gamma}{r}\cos\theta$ **B** $\frac{\gamma}{r\cos\theta}$ **C** $\frac{2\gamma}{r\sin\theta}$ **D** $\frac{4\gamma}{r}\sin\theta$ **E** $\frac{2\gamma}{r\cos\theta}$

B15 It is possible to produce a fairly stable vertical film of soap solution but not one of pure water. Which of the following statements is the reason for it?

A The angles of contact are different
B Water is denser than soap solution
C The surface tension of soap solution can vary at different points in the film but that of pure water cannot
D Soap solution has a larger surface tension than pure water
E Water is incompressible

B16 Two soap bubbles coalesce. It is noticed that, whilst joined together, the radii of the two bubbles are a and b, where $a > b$. The radius of the interface between the two bubbles will be

A $a - b$ **B** $2(a - b)$ **C** $a + b$ **D** $\dfrac{ab}{a+b}$ **E** $\dfrac{ab}{a-b}$

B17 A soap bubble is very slowly blown on the end of a glass tube by a mechanical pump which supplies a fixed volume of air every minute whatever the pressure against which it is pumping. The excess pressure Δp inside the bubble varies with time as shown by which graph?

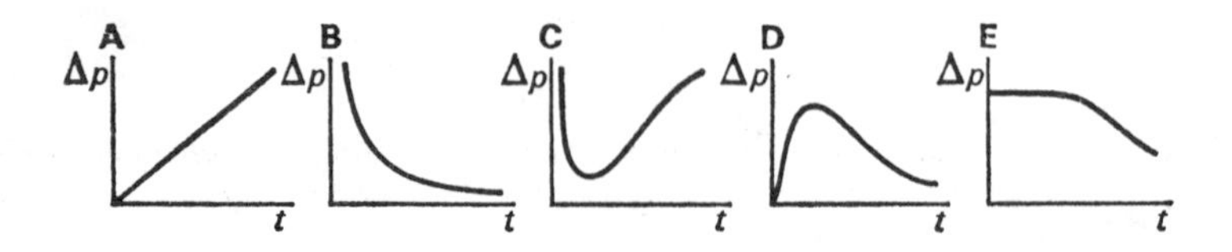

B18 A circular pool of mercury stands on a horizontal table. The density of mercury is ρ and its surface tension γ. The angle of contact between the mercury and the table is $(180 - \alpha)$–see diagram.

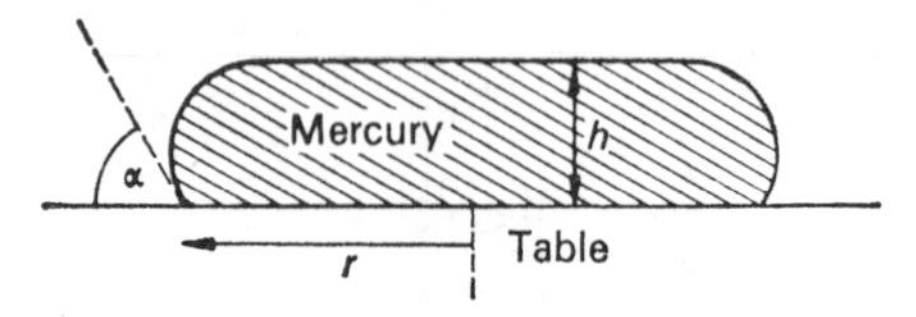

The weight of the mercury is

A $\pi r^2 h\rho g$
B $\pi r^2 h\rho g - 2\pi r\gamma \sin\alpha$
C $\pi r^2 h\rho g - 2\pi r\gamma \cos\alpha$
D $\pi r^2 h\rho g + 2\pi r\gamma \sin\alpha$
E $\pi r^2 h\rho g + 2\pi r\gamma \cos\alpha$

B19 A soap bubble of initial radius r is to be blown up. The surface tension of the soap film is γ. The surface energy needed to double the diameter of the bubble without change of temperature is

A $4\pi r^2\gamma$ **B** $8\pi r^2\gamma$ **C** $12\pi r^2\gamma$ **D** $16\pi r^2\gamma$ **E** $24\pi r^2\gamma$

B20 The diagram shows a section (of length b) of a liquid meniscus touching a

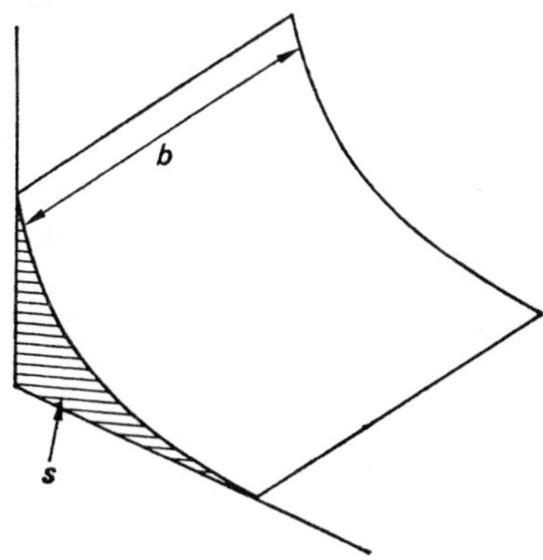

vertical plate. If the surface tension is γ, the angle of contact θ, the density of the liquid ρ and the cross-sectional area of the meniscus S, then S is equal to

A $\dfrac{\gamma\cos\theta}{\rho g}$ **B** $\dfrac{\gamma\cos\theta}{b\rho g}$ **C** $\dfrac{\gamma b}{\rho g\cos\theta}$ **D** $\dfrac{\gamma}{\rho g\cos\theta}$ **E** $\dfrac{\gamma b\cos\theta}{\rho g}$

B21 Mercury is poured into a very wide vertical tube; when it *starts* to enter the horizontal glass capillary tube, of internal radius r, it has reached a height h

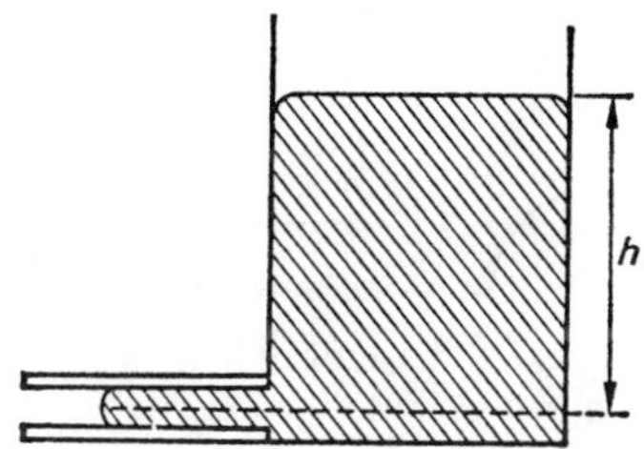

in the wide tube. If the density of mercury is ρ, its surface tension γ and the angle of contact it makes with glass is 130°, then

A $\dfrac{2\gamma}{r}\cos 130° = h\rho g$

B $-\dfrac{2\gamma}{r\cos 130°} = h\rho g$

C $\dfrac{2\gamma}{r}\cos 130° = -h\rho g$

D $\dfrac{2\gamma}{r\cos 130°} = h\rho g$

E $\dfrac{2\gamma}{r} = h\rho g$

B22 The diagram is a highly enlarged view of a very small air bubble trapped and slightly flattened by the surface of soapy water of surface tension γ.

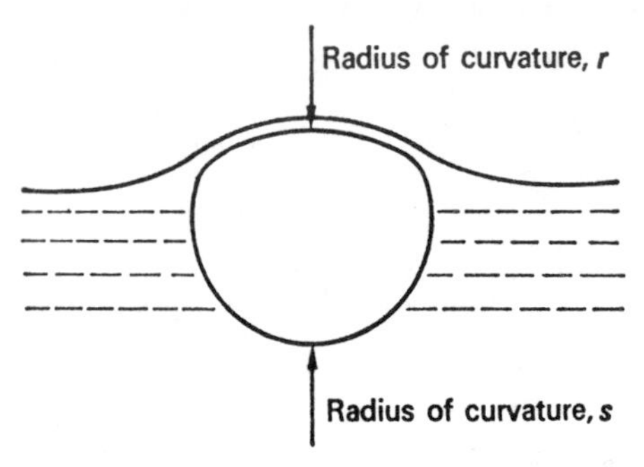

Writing P for atmospheric pressure, the air pressure in the bubble is

A $P+\frac{\gamma}{s}$ **B** $P+\frac{2\gamma}{r}$ **C** $P+\frac{4\gamma}{s}$ **D** $P+\frac{4\gamma}{r}$ **E** $P+\frac{4\gamma}{r}+\frac{2\gamma}{s}$

B23 A thin metal disc may be floated on water. It then displaces a weight Y of water immediately above it, and a weight X where the water surface is bent down-

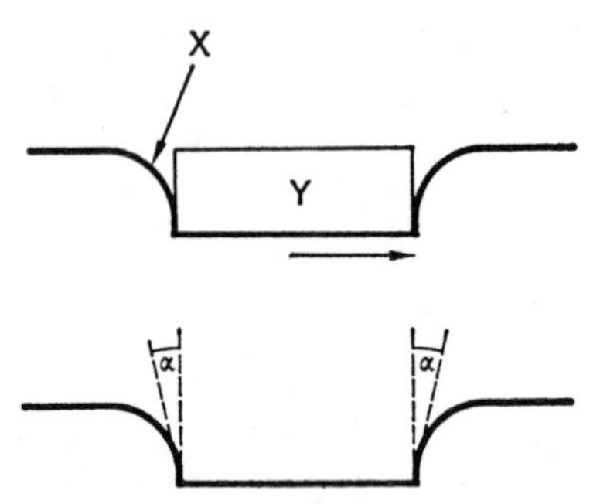

wards along its perimeter. If the surface tension is γ and the radius of the disc r, when in equilibrium the weight of the disc is

A Y **B** $X+Y$ **C** $X+Y-2\pi r\gamma\cos\alpha$ **D** $2\pi r\gamma\cos\alpha$
E $X+Y+2\pi r\gamma\cos\alpha$

B24 Lengths X and Y are cut from a piece of capilliary tubing of uniform bore, and the top of Y is sealed so as to form a small bulb. When both lengths are held vertical and allowed *just* to touch the surface of water in a beaker, the meniscus rises to the point Q in tube X. In tube Y

A the air emerges a little from the bottom of the tube to form part of a small bubble
B the air does not move at all
C the water meniscus rises to the point P
D the water meniscus rises to the point Q
E the water meniscus rises to the point R

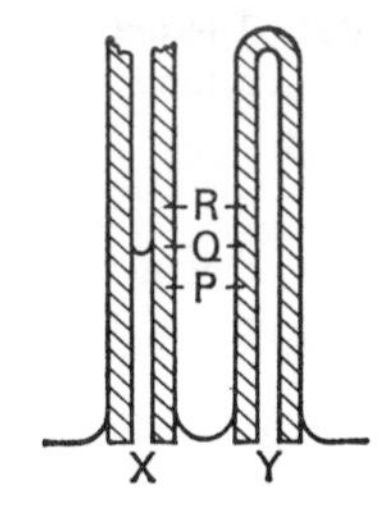

Elasticity

B25 A metal wire is stretched and a graph plotted of the extending force, F, against

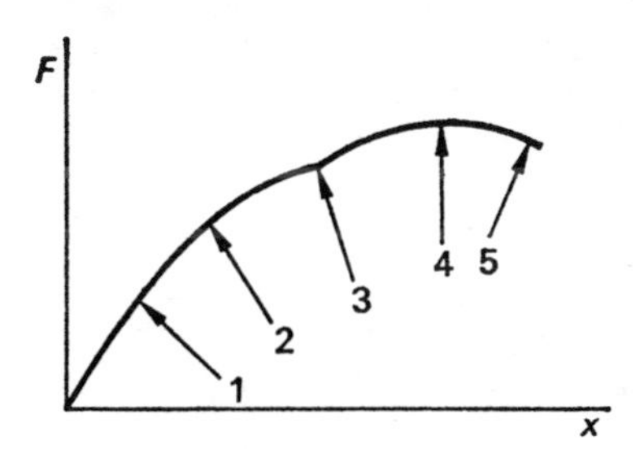

the extension x. The elastic limit is indicated on the graph by the point labelled

A 1 **B** 2 **C** 3 **D** 4 **E** 5

B26 A force of 120 N extends 2.0 m of steel wire by 3.0 mm, while a force of 80 N extends 2.5 m of brass wire, whose diameter is twice that of the steel wire by 1.0 mm. If both wires obey Hooke's law, the ratio of Young's modulus for steel to that for brass is

A 1:5 **B** 2:5 **C** 3:5 **D** 4:5 **E** 8:5

B27 A copper wire and a steel wire are joined together end to end and are hung vertically with the copper wire anchored to a point in the ceiling. The steel wire has half the cross-sectional area and is twice as long as the copper wire. A large mass is hung on the end of the steel wire. The ratio $\frac{\text{stress in copper wire}}{\text{stress in steel wire}}$ is

A 4 **B** 2 **C** 1 **D** $\frac{1}{2}$ **E** none of these

B28 The graph shows the extension, x, of a length of copper wire produced by a force, F, as this is gradually increased.

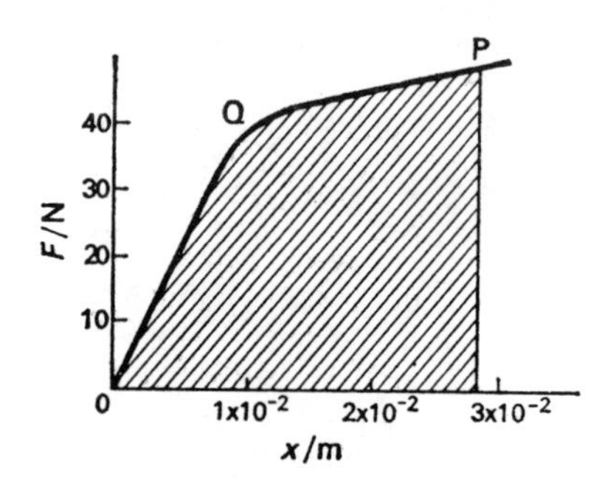

1 At P, the elastic potential energy stored in the wire is represented by the shaded area beneath the graph
2 If, at P, the force is gradually reduced, the graph is retraced back to the origin
3 If the experiment is repeated with twice this length of the copper wire, then a force of 80 N will be needed before the stage indicated by the point Q is reached
4 The wire is still uniform in section at P; i.e. no neck has formed.

B29 The graph shows the behaviour of a length of steel wire in the region for which

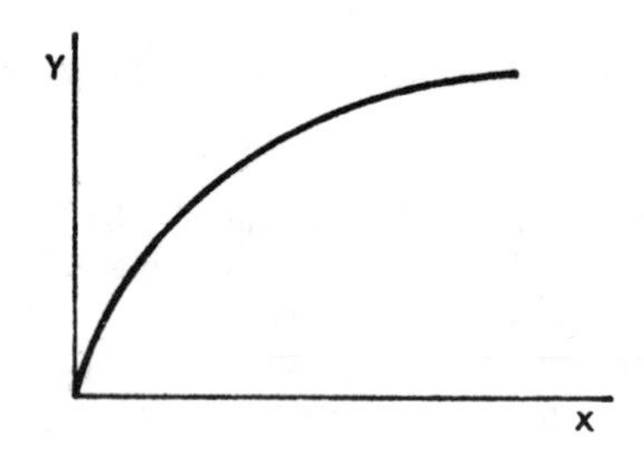

the wire obeys Hooke's law. The graph is part of a parabola. The variables x and y *might* represent

A $x =$ stored elastic energy; $y =$ tension
B $x =$ stress; $y =$ strain
C $x =$ strain; $y =$ stress
D $x =$ strain; $y =$ actual length of the wire
E $x =$ strain; $y =$ stored elastic energy

B30 When an elastic material, with Young's modulus E, is subjected to a stretching stress σ, the elastic energy stored per unit volume of the material is

A $\sigma E/2$ **B** $\sigma^2 E/2$ **C** $\sigma^2/2E$ **D** $\sigma/2E$ **E** $\sigma^2 E^2/2$

B31 The graph shows a force-extension graph for a rubber band. The graph produced during the contraction does not coincide with that during the extension.

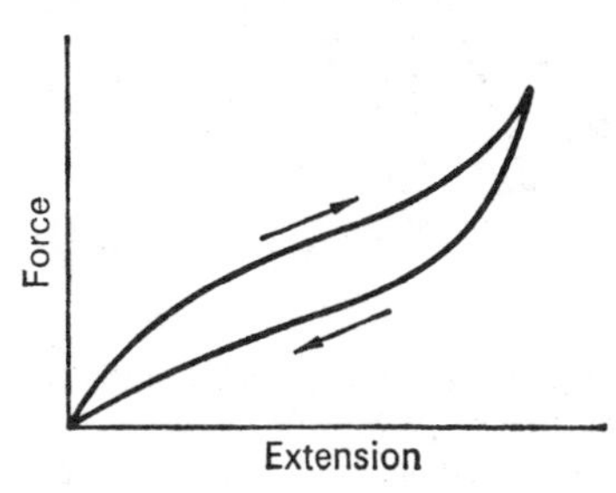

We can deduce that

1 it is easier to compress a block of rubber than to expand it
2 a rubber band does not return to its original length after stretching
3 rubber is a crystalline material
4 a rubber band will be warmed up if stretched and released many times

Fluids in motion

B32 The human heart pumps 1.2×10^{-4} m^3 s^{-1} of blood. The static pressure difference between the outgoing and incoming blood is about 2×10^4 N m^{-2}. If the efficiency of the heart as a pump is only 20 per cent, the total power generated by the heart is

A 0.48 W **B** 2.4 W **C** 4.8 W **D** 12 W **E** 60 W

B33 A gas flows along the tube shown in the next question. The density of the gas in the left side of the tube ρ_1, and in the right side is ρ_2.

A ρ_2/ρ_1 is unrelated to A_1, A_2, v_1 and v_2
B ρ_2/ρ_1 depends on A_1/A_2 but not on the speeds v_1 and v_2
C ρ_2/ρ_1 depends on v_1/v_2 but not on the the areas A_1 and A_2
D ρ_2/ρ_1 depends on $A_1 v_2/A_2 v_1$
E ρ_2/ρ_1 depends on $A_1 v_1/A_2 v_2$

B34 An incompressible liquid flows along the pipe shown in the diagram.

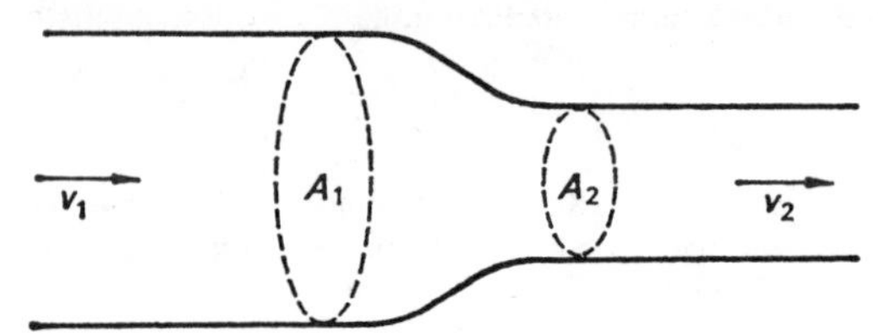

The ratio of the speeds $\frac{v_2}{v_1}$ is equal to

A $\sqrt{\frac{A_1}{A_2}}$ **B** $\sqrt{\frac{A_2}{A_1}}$ **C** $\frac{A_1}{A_2}$ **D** $\frac{A_2}{A_1}$ **E** 1

B35 An incompressible fluid travels as shown in the figure.

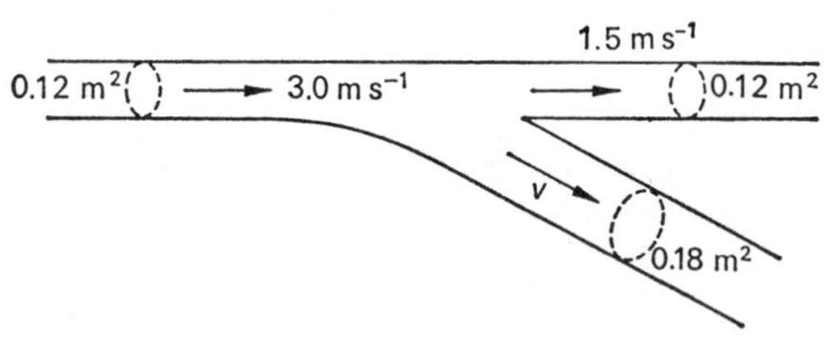

The speed of the fluid, v, in the lower branch will be

A 1.0 m s^{-1} **B** 1.5 m s^{-1} **C** 2.25 m s^{-1} **D** 3.0 m s^{-1} **E** 4.5 m s^{-1}

B36 Water flows through a frictionless duct with a cross-section varying as shown.

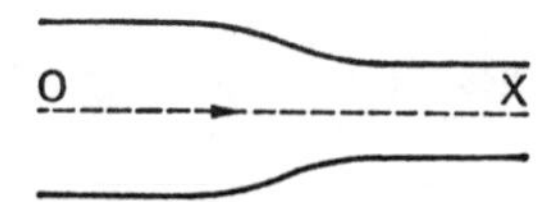

The variation of static pressure P at points along the axis is represented by curve

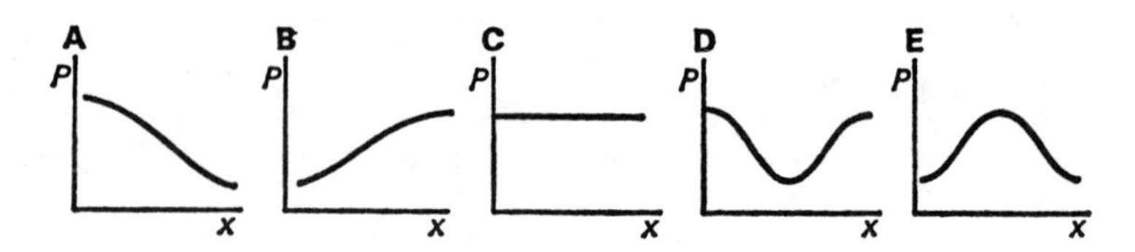

B37 Air from the cylinder is allowed to escape at P. On opening the tap T further so increasing the flow of air past the constriction C in the pipe,

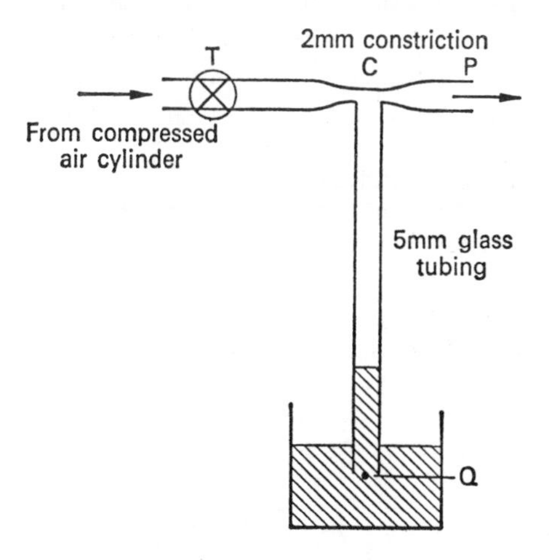

A the mercury climbs higher up the tube
B the mercury falls a little in the tube but remains above Q
C the air bubbles out at Q at the same rate
D the air bubbles out at Q at a slower rate
E the air bubbles out at Q at a faster rate

B38 The diagram shows a spinning ball moving through air. The flow of air is indicated by the streamlines. The relation between the direction of motion of the ball *relative to the air* and the spin of the ball could be

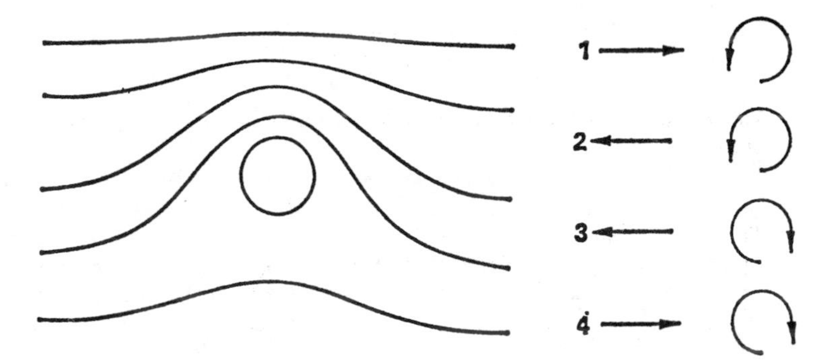

B39 A wooden ball and a steel ball of the same diameter are dropped down the well of a tall block of flats from the fourth floor. Which of the following is *not* a possible reason why the steel ball reaches the ground floor first?

A Air is a viscous fluid
B The push of the air on the wood is greater than the push of air on the steel when they are moving at the same speed
C Steel has a larger density than wood
D The steel ball was projected downwards
E The push of the air on the wood is larger relative to its weight than the push of the air on the steel to its weight

B40 The diagram shows a cup of tea seen from above. The tea has been stirred and is now rotating without turbulence. A graph showing the speed v at

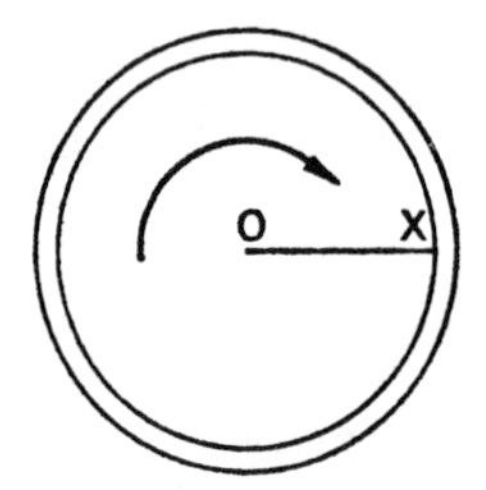

which the liquid is crossing points a distance x from O along a radius OX would look like

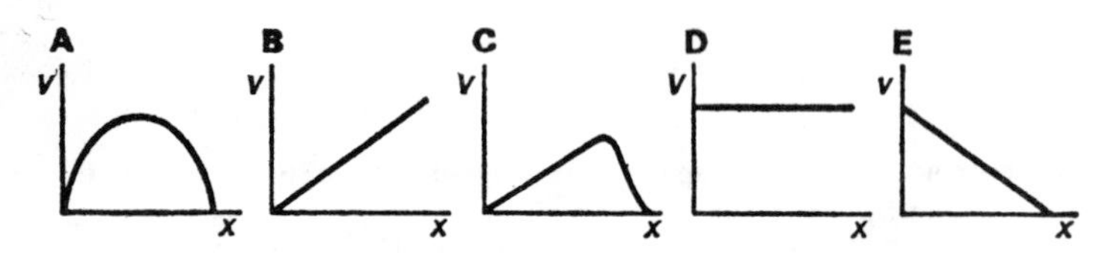

B41 A drop of radius a is falling through air of density ρ and viscosity η at a speed v. Using dimensional analysis, the resistive force F on the drop *might* be proportional to

1 $a\rho v$ **2** $a^2\rho v^2$ **3** $a^2\eta v^2$ **4** $a\eta v$

B42 The onset of turbulent motion in an incompressible liquid flowing in a tube of circular cross-section depends upon a constant, k, called Reynolds' number. This pure *number* is about 2300. If k depends only on the viscosity of the liquid, η, the density of the liquid, ρ, the radius of the tube, a, and the speed at which the liquid is flowing v, then (from a dimensional analysis)

A $k = a\rho v\eta$ **B** $k = a\rho v/\eta$ **C** $k = a\rho\eta/v$ **D** $k = a\rho^2\eta/v$ **E** $k = a\rho v^2/\eta$

B43 The viscous liquid in the boiling tube slowly fills the small floating syringe via a short length PQ, of capillary tubing. The level climbs from X to Y in 30 seconds.
It will now climb from Y to Z in slightly over 30 seconds
BECAUSE
the pressure at P is falling *and* the pressure at Q is rising.

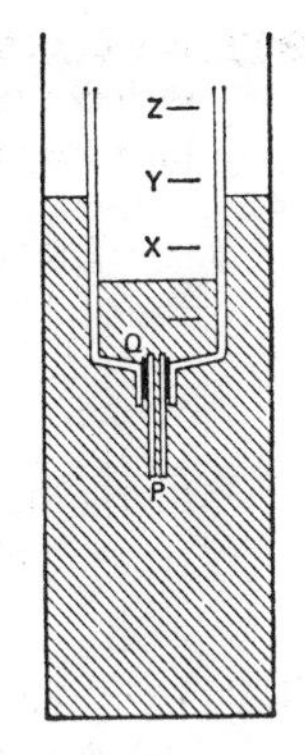

B44 One pattern of viscometer uses a plate with a shallow conical surface. This plate is spun on its central point which rests on a stationary horizontal plate.

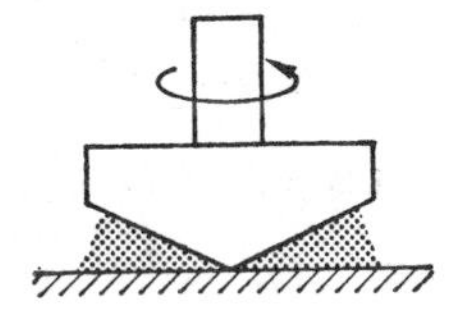

The gap between the plates, which widens steadily away from the centre, is filled with a viscous fluid. The vertical velocity gradient in this fluid

A is proportional to s (the distance from the centre)
B is proportional to s^2
C is inversely proportional to s
D is inversely proportional to s^2
E is independent of s

B45 As a spherical air bubble rises slowly through a viscous liquid it gradually expands.
1 The fluid upthrust on the bubble falls
2 The viscous drag on the bubble increases
3 The speed of the bubble falls
4 The speed of the bubble rises

Gravitation

B46 A manned satellite is put into an elliptic orbit around the Earth as shown in the diagram. The men in the satellite will *not* feel 'weightless' at C
BECAUSE
they are not travelling in a circle.

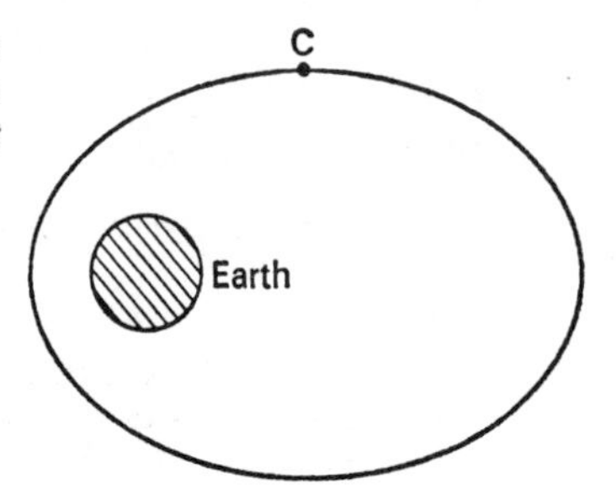

B47 A particle of any mass will start to accelerate downwards at 9.8 m s^{-2} when released from rest at the Earth's surface
BECAUSE
the Earth's gravitational field strength at its surface is 9.8 N kg^{-1}, to 2 sig fig, and is directed downwards.

B48 A meteorite travelling through space directly towards a star experiences, relative to that star

A a uniform acceleration
B a diminishing acceleration
C an acceleration increasing uniformly with time
D an acceleration increasing more and more rapidly with time
E an acceleration proportional to the square of its distance from that star

B49 A hydrogen balloon released on the Moon would

A climb with an acceleration of 9.8×6 m s^{-2}
B climb with an acceleration of 9.8/6 m s^{-2}
C neither climb nor fall
D fall with an acceleration of 9.8×6 m s^{-2}
E fall with an acceleration of 9.8/6 m s^{-2}

(*Note:* the acceleration due to gravity on Earth, 9.8 m s^{-2}, is 6 times that on the Moon)

B50 A massive, uniform sphere has a central, spherical hole in it. A body placed anywhere inside this hole will experience a force, the gravitational pull of the sphere on the body, which is

A directed towards the centre, and of constant size
B directed towards the centre, but increasing in size as the body moves towards the centre
C directed away from the centre, and constant in size; zero at the centre
D directed away from the centre, and increasing in size as the body moves towards the inside walls; zero at the centre
E zero everywhere inside the hole

B51 A satellite moves in a circle around the Earth. The radius of this circle is equal to one half the radius of the Moon's orbit. The satellite completes one revolution in

A 1/2 lunar month **B** $2\sqrt{2}$ lunar months **C** $2^{2/3}$ lunar months

D $2^{-2/3}$ lunar months **E** $2^{-3/2}$ lunar months

(*Note:* a lunar month is the time taken by the Moon to complete one revolution of the Earth)

B52 A satellite skims the Moon's surface in a circular orbit. The acceleration at the Moon's surface due to lunar gravity is $g/6$ and the Moon's radius is $R/4$ (g and R refer similarly to the Earth). If a satellite skimming the Earth has a period of T, the period of revolution of the Moon's satellite will be

A $2/3\,T$ **B** $\sqrt{2/3}\,T$ **C** $\frac{2^2}{3^2}T$ **D** $\frac{3^2}{2^2}T$ **E** $\sqrt{3/2}\,T$

B53 The value of g, the observed acceleration due to gravity, is found to *decline* on moving in the Earth's atmosphere

A towards the poles, or up from the ground
B towards the equator, or up from the ground
C towards the poles, or down towards the ground
D away from latitudes 30° N and 30° S
E away from latitudes 60° N and 60° S

B54 An artificial satellite nears the end of its life as it encounters air resistance. Whilst still in orbit

A it moves faster in a lower orbit
B it moves more slowly in a lower orbit
C it spirals slowly away from the Earth
D it moves faster, but with a longer period of rotation about the Earth
E it moves more slowly, but with a shorter period of rotation about the Earth

B55 Let us write S for the Sun, E for the Earth and M for the Moon. If the distance *ES* is roughly 400 times the distance *EM* and the gravitational pull of S on E is 170 times the gravitational pull of M on E, then S has x times the mass of M where x is roughly

A 6.8×10^4 **B** 7.4×10^5 **C** 1.2×10^7 **D** 2.7×10^7 **E** 4.6×10^9

B56 The angular velocity of the Earth about the Sun reaches a minimum at each full moon
BECAUSE
during the previous two weeks, the gravitational pull of the Moon has operated as a brake to varying extents.

C THERMAL PROPERTIES OF MATTER

Thermometry

C1 A mercury-in-glass thermometer and a platinum resistance thermometer are calibrated linearly from measurements at the ice and steam points. The two thermometers, then, *necessarily* agree

A at every temperature
B only at the calibration points
C at temperatures near zero kelvin
D at temperatures midway between the calibration points
E at the calibration points and one other temperature

C2 A thermocouple, connected to a microvoltmeter, is usually better than a mercury-in-glass thermometer for measuring rapid fluctuations in the temperature of the air, because its sensitive head (matched with the thermometer's)

1 does not need encapsulating in glass
2 has a smaller linear expansivity
3 has a lower heat capacity
4 is a poorer conductor of heat

C3 The upper and lower fixed points of the Celsius thermometric scale are taken to be the melting and boiling points of pure water under specified conditions because

1 thermometric properties always vary linearly between these temperatures
2 changes in pressure do not affect these temperatures
3 all thermometers agree at these temperatures
4 the two situations may be reproduced to the necessary accuracy fairly easily

C4 The bulb of a mercury-in-glass thermometer which is at room temperature is put into boiling water. The mercury level in the stem of the thermometer falls initially, before rising
BECAUSE
the glass forming the bulb expands before the mercury inside the bulb expands.

Calorimetry

C5 In an experiment with a continuous flow calorimeter to find the specific heat capacity of a liquid an input power of 60 W produced a rise of 10 K in the liquid. On doubling the power the same temperature rise was achieved by trebling the rate of flow of the liquid. The power lost to the surroundings in each case was

A 20 W **B** 30 W **C** 40 W **D** 60 W **E** 120 W

C6 If the specific heat capacity of the liquid in question **C5** was 2.0 kJ kg^{-1} K^{-1}, the initial rate of flow was

A 0.75×10^{-3} kg s^{-1} **B** 1.25×10^{-3} kg s^{-1} **C** 1.50×10^{-3} kg s^{-1}
D 3.00×10^{-3} kg s^{-1} **E** 4.00×10^{-3} kg s^{-1}

C7 A block of metal X, mass m, at 0 °C comes into contact with another metal block Y, of mass $2m$, at 100 °C. Heat conduction takes place with no loss to the surroundings, and the final equilibrium temperature of the blocks is 20 °C. If the specific heat capacities of the two metals are c_x and c_y respectively, then

A $c_x = 8\,c_y$ **B** $c_x = 4\,c_y$ **C** $c_x = 2\,c_y$ **D** $c_x = \frac{1}{2}\,c_y$ **E** $c_x = \frac{1}{4}\,c_y$

C8 Insulated solid blocks, X and Y, of different metals, are drilled out as shown,

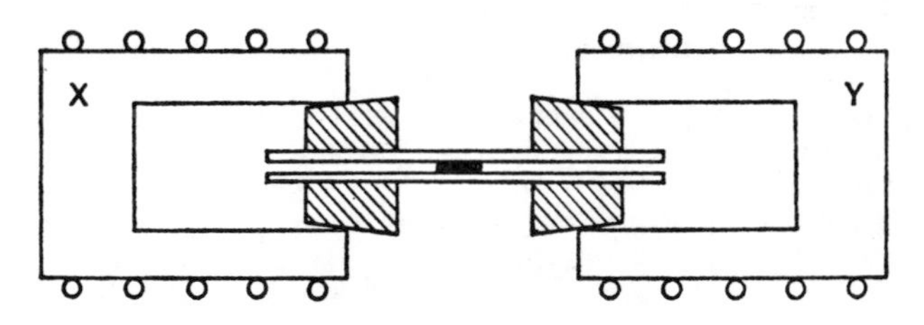

and a mercury index used to match the pressures of the two small volumes of trapped air. If the two heating coils keep the index stationary, then

1 both blocks contain the same mass of air
2 the power, P_x, supplied to X equals the power, P_y, supplied to Y
3 the heat capacity, C_x, of X, equals the heat capacity, C_y, of Y
4 the ratio $\frac{C_x}{C_y}$ equals the ratio $\frac{P_x}{P_y}$

C9 At the triple point

1 a substance can exist with solid, liquid and gaseous forms all in equilibrium
2 the specific latent heat of fusion is zero
3 no change in volume occurs on melting or evaporation
4 the specific latent heat of vaporisation is zero

The gas laws

C10 A mass of liquid with volume V_1 turns into volume V_2 of gas as it evaporates against a constant external pressure p. The specific latent heat of vaporisation, L, includes energy needed to overcome intermolecular forces of attraction, amounting to

A $pV_2 - pV_1$ **B** $pV_2 + pV_1$ **C** $L - pV_2 + pV_1$ **D** $L + pV_2 - pV_1$
E $L - pV_2 - pV_1$

C11 A mass M of metal requires an input power P to keep it just molten. When the heater is switched off the metal completely solidifies in a time Δt. If the rate of loss of heat to the surroundings is constant, then the specific latent heat of fusion of the metal is

A $\frac{P}{M\Delta t}$ **B** $\frac{\Delta t}{PM}$ **C** $\frac{PM}{\Delta t}$ **D** $PM\Delta t$ **E** $\frac{P\Delta t}{M}$

C12 The expansion of unit mass of a perfect gas at constant pressure is shown in the diagram where,

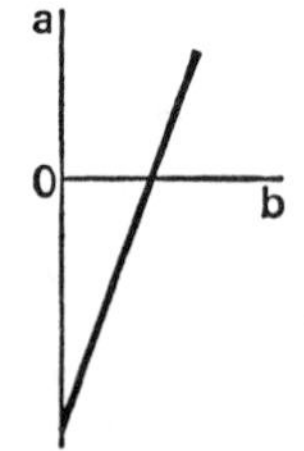

A a = volume, b = common temperature (°C)
B a = volume, b = temperature (K)
C a = common temperature (°C), b = volume
D a = temperature (K), b = volume
E the gradient of the graph is faulty

C13 The expansion of a mass m of an ideal gas at a constant pressure p is shown by the line H. The expansion of a mass $2m$ of the same gas, at a pressure $p/2$ is shown by

A line F **B** line G **C** line H **D** line J **E** line K

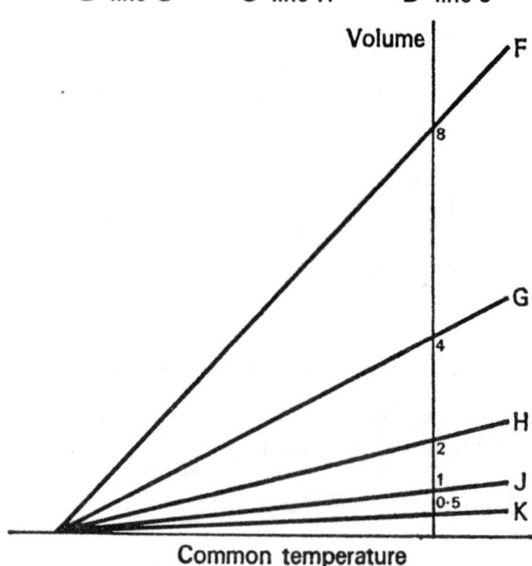

C14 For an ideal gas, the specific heat capacity at constant volume is more than the specific heat capacity at constant pressure
BECAUSE
at constant volume, additional energy is needed to prevent expansion as the pressure rises.

C15 P contains an ideal gas at a pressure of 5×10^5 N m^{-2} and a temperature of 300 K. It is connected by a thin tube to container Q of four times the volume of

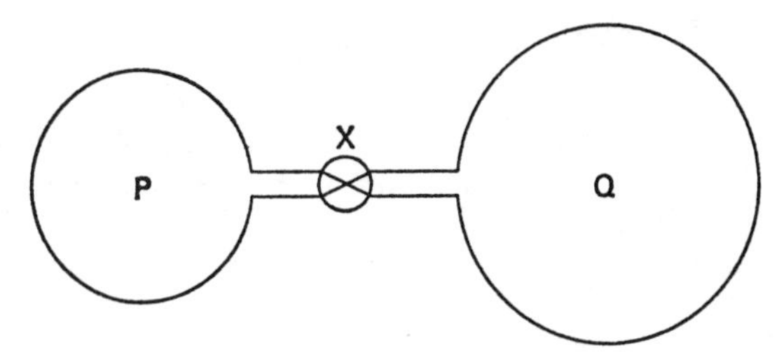

P. Q contains the same ideal gas at a pressure of 10^5 N m^{-2} and a temperature of 400 K. The connecting tap X is opened, and equilibrium achieved while the temperature of each container is *kept constant at its initial value.* The final pressure in the system is y $\times$ 10^5 N m^{-2} where y is equal to

A 1.0 **B** 1.8 **C** 2.0 **D** 2.6 **E** 3.2

C16 A cycle pump delivers a volume V of air at each stroke. The atmospheric pressure is P. Forty strokes of the pump are needed to blow up a rubber balloon (initially flat) to a volume of $20V$ at room temperature. The force per unit length across a line drawn in the surface of the balloon is T, and the balloon's radius is r. Therefore

A $\frac{T}{r} = P$ **B** $\frac{2T}{r} = P$ **C** $\frac{4T}{r} = P$ **D** $\frac{T}{r} = 2P$ **E** $\frac{T}{r} = 4P$

Molecular motions

C17 In the expression $p = \frac{1}{3}\rho\overline{c^2}$ for the pressure p of an ideal gas,

1 1/3 is an approximation for $1/\pi$
2 ρ is the mass per unit volume of the gas
3 $\sqrt{\overline{c^2}}$ is the average speed of the molecules
4 the appropriate unit for $\rho\overline{c^2}/3$ is N m^{-2}

C18 The root mean square speed of a group of N gas molecules, having speeds $c_1, c_2, c_3 \ldots c_n$, is

A $\frac{1}{N}\sqrt{(c_1 + c_2 + c_3 \ldots + c_n)^2}$ B $\frac{1}{N}\sqrt{c_1^2 + c_2^2 + c_3^2 \ldots + c_n^2}$

C $\sqrt{\frac{1}{N}(c_1^2 + c_2^2 + c_3^2 \ldots + c_n^2)}$ D $\sqrt{\left(\frac{c_1 + c_2 + c_3 \ldots + c_n}{N}\right)^2}$

E $\sqrt{\frac{1}{N}(c_1 + c_2 + c_3 \ldots + c_n)^2}$

C19 The *total* kinetic energy of a group of N gas molecules, each of mass m, with speeds $c_1, c_2, c_3 \ldots c_n$ (giving a root mean square speed c_{rms}) is

A $\frac{1}{2}m(Nc_{rms})^2$ B $\frac{1}{2}Nm(c_1^2 + c_2^2 + c_3^2 \ldots + c_n^2)$

C $\frac{1}{2}m(c_1^2 + c_2^2 + c_3^2 \ldots + c_n^2)$ D $\frac{1}{2}mc^2_{rms}$ E $\frac{1}{2}mc_{rms}$

C20 The oxygen molecule has 16 times the mass of the hydrogen molecule. At room temperature, then, the ratio

$$\left(\frac{\text{root mean square speed of oxygen molecules}}{\text{root mean square speed of hydrogen molecules}}\right)$$

is given, by the simple kinetic theory of gases, as

A 16 B 4 C 2 D $\frac{1}{4}$ E $\frac{1}{16}$

C21 Given that the density of argon (an ideal gas) at a pressure of 10^5 N m^{-2} and a temperature of 270 K is 2.70 kg m^{-3}, the mean square speed of the atoms is

A $\frac{3 \times 10^5}{2.7}$ m^2 s^{-2} B $\frac{2.7 \times 10^5}{3}$ m^2 s^{-2}

C $\frac{2.7 \times 3}{10^5}$ m^2 s^{-2} D $\frac{270 \times 10^5}{2.7}$ m^2 s^{-2}

E $3 \times 10^5 \times 2.7$ m^2 s^{-2}

C22 Some cigarette smoke is trapped in a small glass container, strongly illuminated and viewed through a microscope. A large number of very small smoke particles is seen, in continuous random motion as a result of their bombardment by air molecules. If the mass of a smoke particle is about 10^{12} times the mass of an air molecule, the average speed of a smoke particle is about x times the average speed of an air molecule, where x is

A 10^{-12} B 10^{-6} C 1 D 10^6 E 10^{12}

Vapours

C23 When a pool of liquid is evaporating in an open dish

1 the temperature of the liquid will drop unless heat enters the liquid
2 the liquid will evaporate more quickly if a stream of dry air is blown over the surface of the liquid
3 the liquid will evaporate more slowly as its surface area shrinks
4 the liquid will evaporate more quickly if the (dry) air above it is compressed without change of temperature

C24 The graphs show some of the isothermals obtained by Andrews for carbon dioxide.

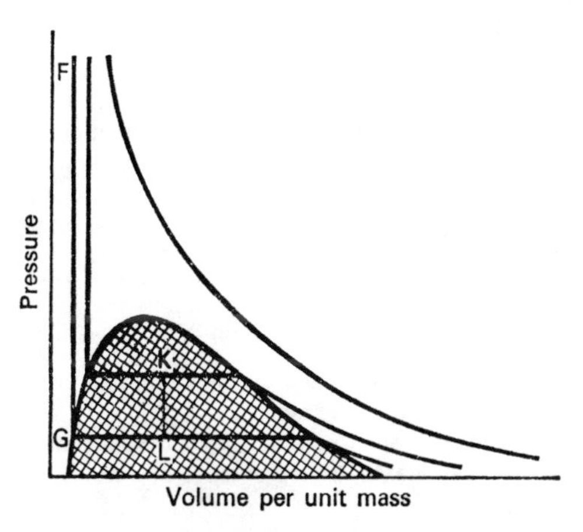

1 Vapour appeared at the surface of the liquid only in the shaded area.
2 The vapour at K has the same density as that at L
3 The liquid condenses with noticeably different densities at different temperatures
4 The straight line FG indicates agreement with Boyle's Law in this region

C25 A small air bubble remains attached to the bottom surface inside a beaker of cold water. As the water is warmed, it swells. Contributory factors are

1 an increase in the saturated vapour pressure of water
2 an increase in the root mean square speed of the air molecules in the bubble
3 a decrease in the surface tension of water
4 a decrease in the viscosity of water

C26 When a beaker containing some clean mercury has stood at room temperature for several minutes, the air in it carries an appreciable trace of mercury vapour, which will cast a shadow on a fluorescent screen when illuminated by a low-intensity mercury-vapour UV lamp. If the beaker is tilted, the shadow of the vapour is seen to pour out within a second or two.

In the above experiment the air which was in the beaker with the mercury vapour, remains behind in the beaker

BECAUSE

a vapour can diffuse through a gas such as air without producing bodily movement of that gas.

Conduction

C27 P and Q are identical well-lagged baths filled with hot water. The surface of P is clean while that of Q is covered with a thick layer of bubbles.

Bath Q will cool more quickly than bath P

BECAUSE

the total surface area of the foam, from which heat is lost to the air, is greater than the surface area of the water in bath P.

C28 The energy flow by conduction along a uniform lagged bar

1 is proportional to the temperature gradient along the bar
2 may be expressed in watts per metre
3 is proportional to the thermal conductivity of the material of the bar
4 is inversely proportional to its area of cross-section

C29 In a copper bar whose ends are maintained at different temperatures, the energy is conducted to the cooler end by

1 the motion of free electrons
2 the migration of high energy molecules to the cooler end
3 the interchange of vibrational energy between adjacent atoms
4 the random movement of electrons and atoms through the bar

C30 A sphere of density ρ, specific heat capacity c, and radius r, is hung on a thermally insulating thread in an enclosure which is kept at a lower temperature than the sphere. The temperature of the sphere starts to drop at a rate which depends upon the temperature difference between the sphere and the enclosure and the nature of the surface of the sphere, and is also proportional to

A $\frac{c}{r^3\rho}$ **B** $\frac{1}{r^3\rho c}$ **C** $r^3\rho c$ **D** $\frac{1}{r\rho c}$

E some other function of r, ρ, and c

C31 A double-glazed window consists of two parallel sheets of glass of equal thickness, between which is trapped a layer of still air. In which diagram is the variation of the temperature (plotted vertically) across the complete window shown correctly?

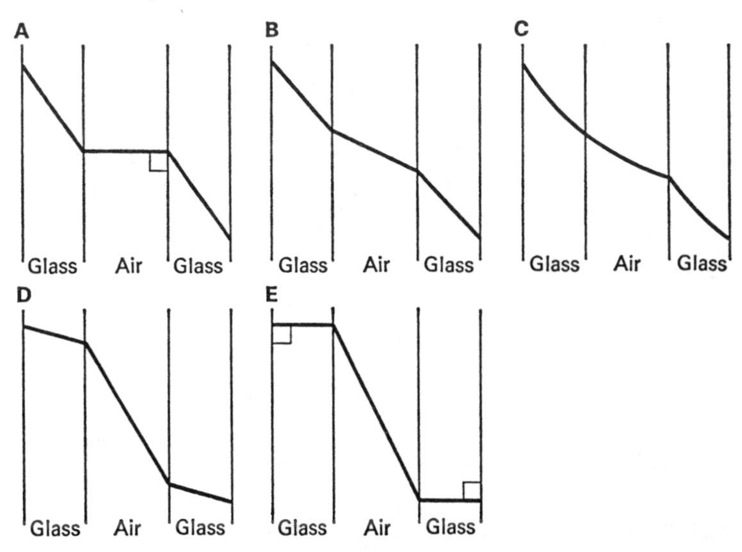

C32 A lagged metal bar, P, of uniform cross-section is heated electrically at one end and cooled at the other by a constant stream of cold water flowing through a spiral tube wrapped around the bar until a steady state is reached. Another bar, Q, of the same dimensions but of twice the thermal conductivity is heated and cooled in exactly the same way by the same electrical power and by the same rate of flow of water.

A The temperature gradient in P is twice that in Q
B The temperature gradient in P is one half that in Q
C The temperature gradient is zero in both bars
D The rise in temperature of the water for P is one half that for Q
E The rise in temperature of the water for P is twice that for Q

C33 Expanded polystyrene is a very poor conductor of heat
BECAUSE
it contains a lot of air pockets and air is a very poor conductor of heat.

C34 With a cold wind keeping the surface at −10 °C, a layer of ice on a pond grows in thickness from 20 mm to 21 mm in ten minutes. Later, with the surface at the same temperature, it will grow from 40 mm to 42 mm in *approximately*

A 10 minutes **B** $10\sqrt{2}$ minutes **C** 20 minutes **D** 40 minutes
E 80 minutes

C35 Using two metal bars of the same dimensions, it is possible to join a large block maintained at a high temperature to a second large block maintained at a low temperature in either of two ways; firstly with the bars in parallel and, secondly, with the bars in series. If the bars have thermal conductivities in the ratio of 2:1, then the rate of flow of heat in the parallel arrangement is *n* times that in the other, where *n* is

A $\frac{1}{4}$ **B** $\frac{1}{2}$ **C** 2 **D** $\frac{9}{2}$ **E** 9

C36 A solid copper bar of negligible electrical resistance is heated at the left hand end, X, and cooled at the other end, Y. An accumulator is connected to it as shown, and passes a heavy direct current along it. The free electrons in the copper bar now

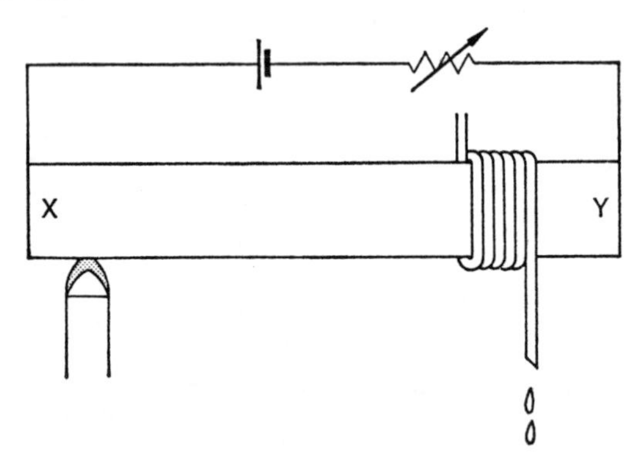

A conduct heat from X to Y via the accumulator
B move from Y to X along the bar, but still pass heat energy from X to Y along the bar
C move from Y to X along the bar, and stop taking any heat at all from X to Y
D move from X to Y along the bar until the current reaches a certain critical value, then stop and reverse
E move away from X by both routes and accumulate steadily at Y

Convection and radiation

C37 When fluids are heated from the bottom, convection currents are produced BECAUSE
heated fluid becomes less dense than the cold fluid above it.

C38 If other things are equal, the temperature of a large solid sphere will drop more quickly than that of a similar but smaller sphere, when both are suspended in cold, evacuated enclosures
BECAUSE
the rate of loss of energy by radiation is proportional to the surface area of the sphere.

C39 All other things being equal, clean snow will melt more quickly in sunlight than dirty snow
BECAUSE
clean snow absorbs sunlight more quickly than dirty snow.

C40 The Stefan-Boltzmann radiation constant, σ, could be measured in the following units

1 $\mathrm{J\,s^{-1}\,m^{-2}\,K^{4}}$ **2** $\mathrm{kg\,s^{-3}\,K^{-4}}$ **3** $\mathrm{N\,m\,s^{-1}\,K^{-4}}$ **4** $\mathrm{W\,m^{-2}\,K^{-4}}$

C41 The naked human body at 304 K emits approximately 200 W by radiation. A naked corpse at room temperature, 288 K, will emit therefore

A $200 \times \frac{288}{304}$ W **B** $200 \times \left(\frac{288}{304}\right)^4$ W **C** 200 W

D zero W **E** $200 \times \frac{16}{304}$ W

D ELECTRIC CIRCUITS

Electrical energy

D1 The smallest number of 10 Ω resistors, each capable of dissipating only 1 W, that can be used to make a 10 Ω resistor able to dissipate 5 W, is

A 5 **B** 9 **C** 12 **D** 16 **E** 25

D2 You are supplied with three separate resistors each of resistance R, and a supply of e.m.f. V. The *possible* rates at which the supply could be made to liberate energy include

1 $\frac{V^2}{R}$ **2** $\frac{V^2}{2R}$ **3** $\frac{V^2}{3R}$ **4** $\frac{V^2}{4R}$

D3 An electric light bulb is marked 240 V, 100 W. When it is operated on a 210 V supply it lasts longer than when operated on 240 V
BECAUSE
its operating temperature is then lower.

D4 A beam of electrons constitutes a current of 10 microamps. Each electron possesses 1.5×10^{-15} J as it hits an anode, and gives up all its energy at impact. If the charge on an electron is 1.6×10^{-19} C then the rate of heat dissipation at the electrode is

A $\dfrac{10^{-5} \times (1.5 \times 10^{-15})}{1.6 \times 10^{-19}}$ W

B $\dfrac{10^{-5} \times (1.6 \times 10^{-19})}{1.5 \times 10^{-15}}$ W

C $\dfrac{10 \times (1.5 \times 10^{-15})}{1.6 \times 10^{-19}}$ W

D $\dfrac{10}{1.5 \times 10^{-15}}$ W

E $\dfrac{10}{1.6 \times 10^{-19}}$ W

Electrical elements

D5 A cell can supply 9600 C in 7200 s. Its capacity is

A $\dfrac{9600 \times 7200}{3600}$ ampere hour

B $\dfrac{9600 \times 3600}{7200}$ ampere hour

C $\dfrac{9600}{3600}$ ampere hour

D $\dfrac{9600}{7200}$ ampere hour

E $\dfrac{9600}{7200 \times 3600}$ ampere hour

D6 A cell with a constant e.m.f. of 1.25 V passes a current which is steady at 0.10 A for 100 hours, and is then exhausted.

1 The capacity of the cell is 10 ampere hours
2 The cell stores 4.5×10^4 J
3 The capacity of the cell would be greater if all of its components had a larger physical volume
4 The e.m.f. of the cell would be greater if all of its components had a larger physical volume

D7 A square piece of polythene sheet measuring 400 mm by 400 mm is coated on each side with conducting paint, and leads are connected to the paint. When the potential difference between the paint layers is 60 V a current of 0.024 μA flows through the polythene. If the resistivity of the polythene is 2×10^{13} Ω m, then one may calculate from these figures

1 the thickness of the polythene
2 the electric current density in the polythene
3 the electric field strength in the polythene
4 the relative permittivity of the polythene

D8 Aluminium and copper rods are designed to have the same length and the same resistance. The resistivity of copper is half that of aluminium, but its density is three times that of aluminium. The ratio of the mass of the aluminium rod to the mass of the copper rod is

A $\frac{1}{2} \times \frac{1}{3}$ **B** $\frac{1}{3}$ **C** $\frac{2}{3}$ **D** $\frac{3}{2}$ **E** 2×3

D9 A cylindrical copper rod is re-formed to twice its original length with no change in volume. If the resistance between its ends was R before the change, it is now

A R **B** $2R$ **C** $4R$ **D** $8R$ **E** R^2

D10 The internal resistance of a cell

1 sets a ceiling to the power available from it in any possible external circuit
2 limits the current which will flow when the cell is short-circuited
3 is determined, in part, by the physical dimensions of the cell
4 falls slowly throughout the life of the cell

D11 Two large parallel plates, separated by a distance d and placed in a vacuum tube, are connected to a power supply with terminal potential difference V. A doubly charged oxygen ion starts from rest on the surface of one plate and is accelerated to the other. The charge on an electron is e. The kinetic energy of the ion when it hits the second plate is

A $\frac{1}{2}eV$ **B** $\frac{eV}{d}$ **C** eVd **D** $\frac{Vd}{e}$ **E** $2eV$

Current/potential difference relationships

D12 A certain student wrote 'Since $R = \frac{V}{I}$, where R is the resistance of a conductor expressed in ohms, V is the potential difference across it expressed in volts, and I is the current through it expressed in amperes, we may deduce that the resistance of a conductor varies in direct proportion with the p.d. across it'.

A This is correct
B The equation is faulty since the term V/I should have been I/V
C The equation is faulty, and should have read $R = V/I + R_0$, where R_0 is the resistance when no current is flowing
D The statement is faulty, since the phrase *in direct proportion* should have read *inversely*
E The logic is false since V and I are not independent variables

D13 The following graphs give the I/V characteristics for various conductors. Which one indicates that the conductor obeys Ohm's law?

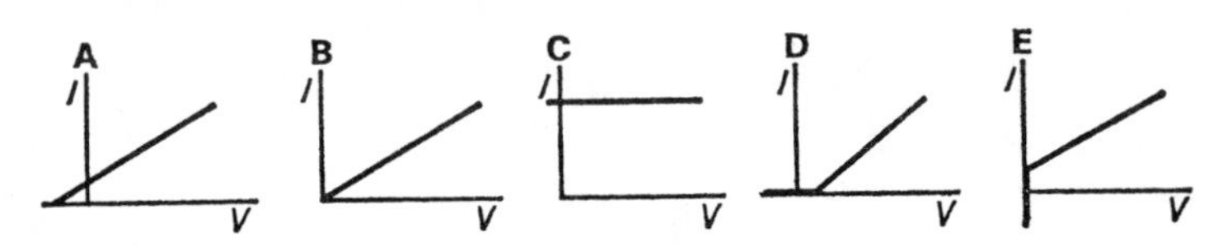

D14 Through which of the following conductors is the current always proportional to the applied potential difference?

1 An electric lamp filament
2 A selenium rectifier
3 A lead-acid cell
4 A metal wire at constant temperature

A model of metallic conduction

D15 A Hall voltage, V_H, is observed across the width of a semiconductor bar by applying a magnetic field with flux density B at 90° to the current I flowing along the bar. V_H may be doubled by keeping other factors constant but

1 warming the semiconductor
2 doubling the value of I
3 doubling the value of B
4 cooling the semiconductor

D16 A beam of identical particles, each carrying a charge Q is moving in a vacuum. If the current at the collecting electrode is I then the number of particles arriving there each second may be found

A immediately, as I/Q
B only if we know the speed of the particles
C only if we know the elementary (electron) charge
D only if we know the area of cross-section of the beam
E only if we know the power dissipated as heat etc. at the electrode

D17 Factors contributing to the climb in resistance of a copper wire with increase in temperature include the following:

1 the conduction electrons collide with each other more frequently
2 the lattice of copper atoms becomes denser
3 the number of conduction electrons decreases
4 the conduction electrons collide with the copper atoms more frequently

D18 When Ohm's law is obeyed by a conductor

1 the number of conduction electrons is unaffected by the current density
2 the power dissipated in it is proportional to the square of the current
3 the drift velocity of the electrons is proportional to the potential gradient along it
4 the conductivity is directly proportional to the applied potential difference

D19 P and Q are two pieces of copper wire of circular cross-section, joined together as shown to form part of a circuit carrying a certain current in the direction from P to Q.

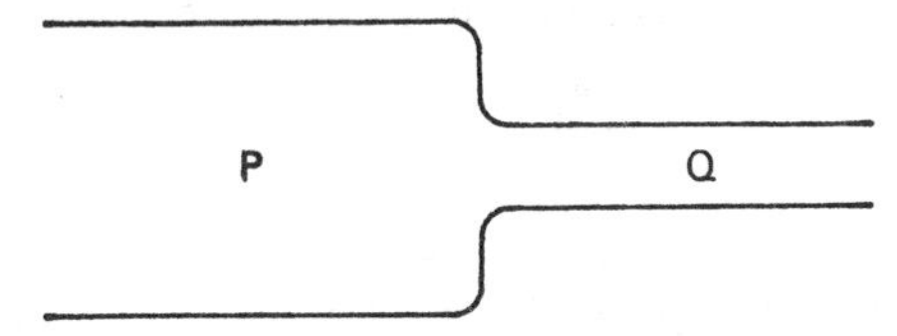

1 Charge accumulates at the junction
2 The conduction electrons in Q have a greater drift velocity than those in P
3 The electric current in Q is greater than that in P
4 In P there are the same number of conduction electrons per unit volume as in Q

D20 There are n free electrons per unit volume in a piece of wire, each electron carrying a charge e. To express their drift velocity in the wire in terms of n and e, we must also have

A the potential gradient in the wire
B the current density in the wire
C the mobility of the electrons in the wire
D the resistivity of the wire
E the length of the wire

D21 PQ and RS are identical lengths of uniform resistance wire which are connected respectively across a 2 V d.c. supply and a 4 V d.c. supply. Both wires are earthed at their mid-points.

1 The mean drift velocity along the wire of the electrons is greater at S than at R
2 There are twice as many conductivity electrons i n RS as in PQ
3 There is a steady leakage current to earth in both circuits
4 The mean drift velocity of the conduction electrons is bigger in RS than in PQ

D22 The characteristics of a zener diode are shown in the first diagram. Two such diodes are taken and connected in series, facing in opposite directions. Which diagram shows the I/V relationship of this combination?

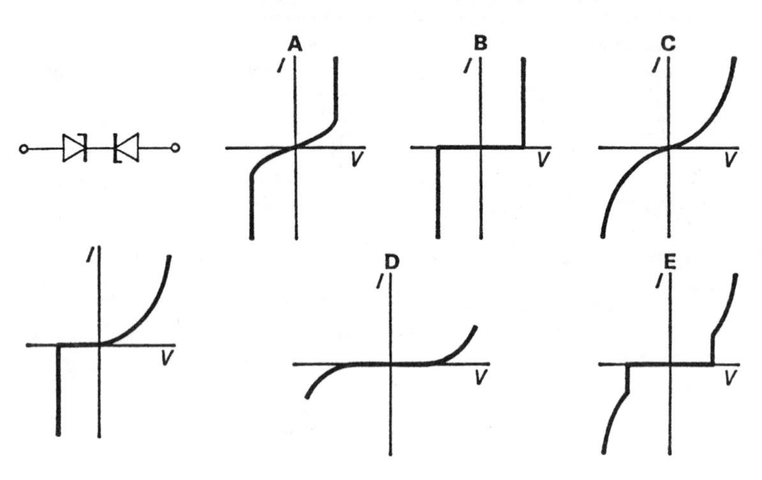

D23 Referring to question **D22**, which diagram shows the I/V relationship of the combination of two zener diodes if these are connected in parallel facing in opposite directions?

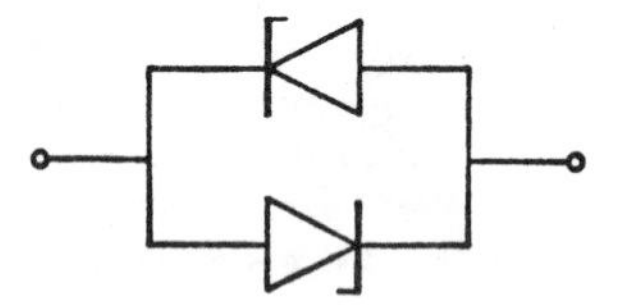

D24 A moving-coil voltmeter, M, reading from zero to 2 V, is fitted with a zener diode having a zener breakdown voltage of 10 V. The diagram shows its characteristics.

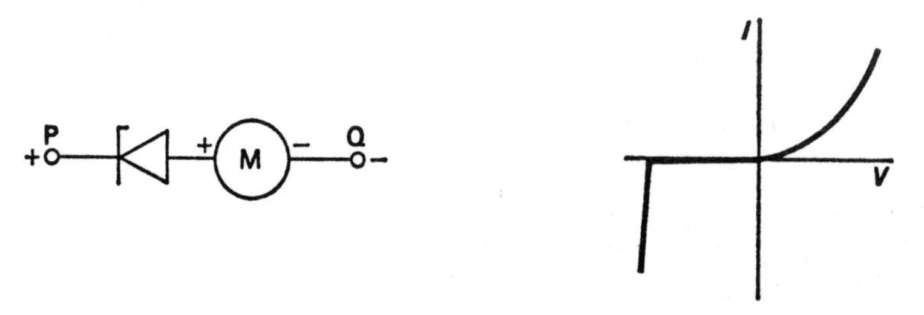

Using the terminals P and Q, the meter should now be calibrated

A 0 to 2 V linearly **B** 0 to 2 V non-linearly **C** 0 to 10 V
D 0 to 12 V **E** 10 V to 12 V

Measuring instruments

D25 Which graph depicts the relationship between the total resistance R of a multi-range moving-coil ammeter and its full-scale deflection, I?

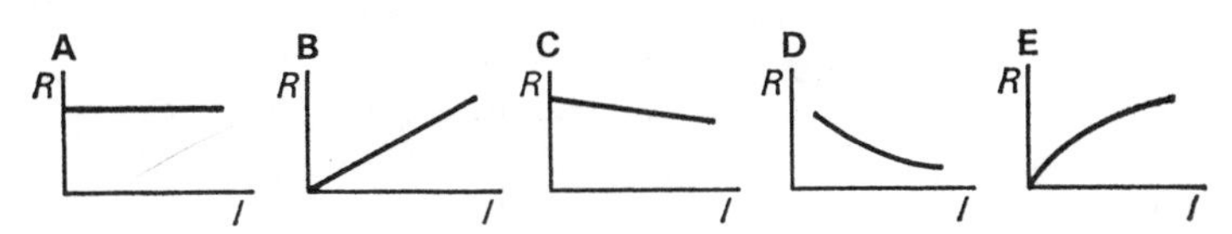

D26 Which graph depicts the relationship between the total resistance R of a multi-range moving-coil voltmeter, and its full-scale deflection, V?

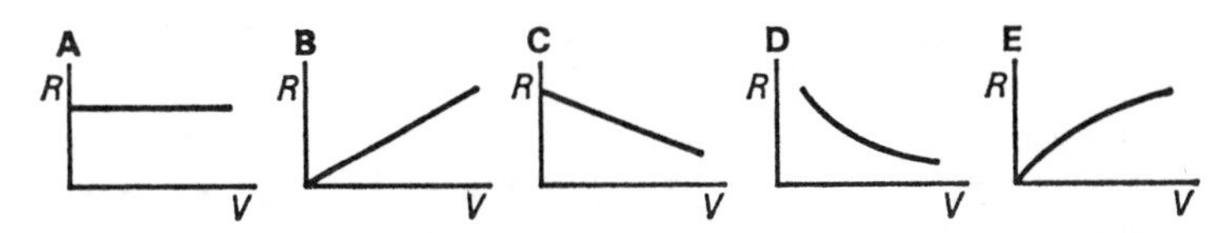

D27 The current required for full-scale deflection in a moving-coil galvanometer depends upon

1 the number of turns used in winding the coil
2 the area of cross section of the coil
3 the magnetic flux density through the coil
4 the stiffness of the springs attached to the coil

D28 Two galvanometers P and Q are identical except for their coils. P has 100 turns of resistance 40 Ω, while Q has 200 turns of resistance 160 Ω. The ratio of their deflections, $\theta_P : \theta_Q$, when connected in turn to a cell of internal resistance 20 Ω, but constant e.m.f., is

A $\frac{160}{40}$ **B** $\frac{160+20}{40+20}$ **C** $\frac{160}{40} \times \frac{200}{100}$ **D** $\frac{160+20}{40+20} \times \frac{200}{100}$

E $\frac{160+20}{40+20} \times \frac{100}{200}$

D29 A person wishes to measure the voltage of a d.c. supply which is known to be about 250 V. He has two voltmeters available, connects them in series across the supply and adds their indications together.

If their current sensitivities are different, this method is invalid
BECAUSE
both instruments are being made to carry the same current.

D30 An alternating current varies with time as shown. The average current read by a moving coil d.c. instrument is

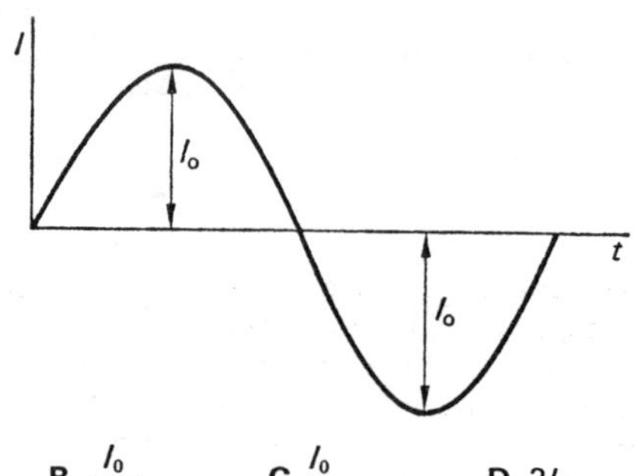

A zero **B** $\frac{I_0}{\sqrt{2}}$ **C** $\frac{I_0}{\pi}$ **D** $2I_0$

E some other fraction of I_0

D31 In which of the following instances does the moving-coil galvanometer, G, register a steady deflection (not necessarily the true current) when an a.c. supply is connected to X and Y?

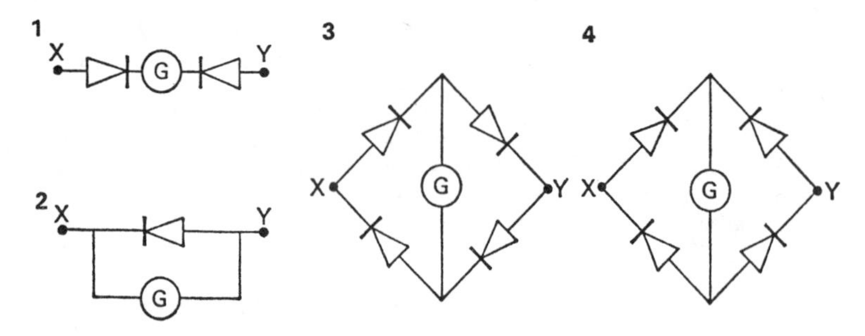

D32 A meter capable of measuring alternating current *could* depend upon

1. the interaction between a suspended coil and a fixed coil, through both of which the current passes
2. the expansion of a wire through which the current passes
3. the interaction between two pieces of metal in which the current induces magnetic poles
4. the interaction between a suspended coil through which the current passes and a permanent magnet

Circuit problems

D33 A single closed loop of resistance wire is mounted on a copper rod at T. As the sliding contact shown as P moves round the semi-circle PQRST, the resistance between the sliding contact and T varies as shown. (Resistance is plotted vertically.)

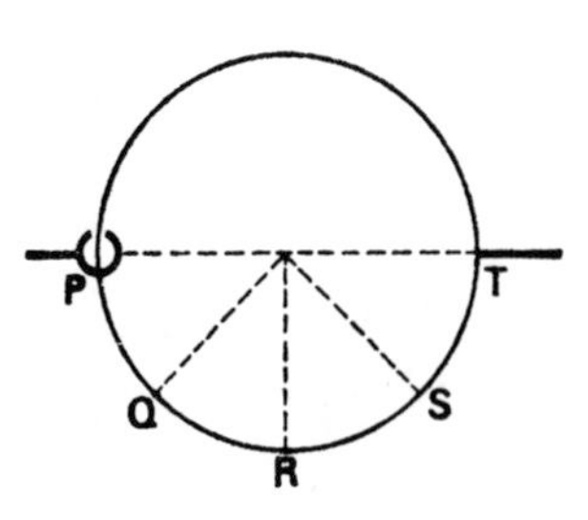

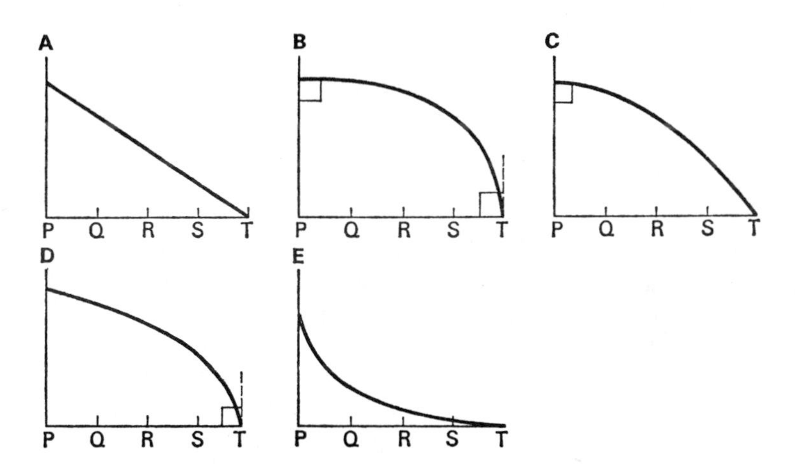

D34 A current of 0.5 A is caused to pass through a resistor and cell as shown. The e.m.f. of the cell is 2 V, and it has zero internal resistance.

1 a is at a higher potential than c
2 b is at a higher potential than c
3 The potential difference between a and b is 1.0 V
4 The potential difference between a and c is 1.0 V

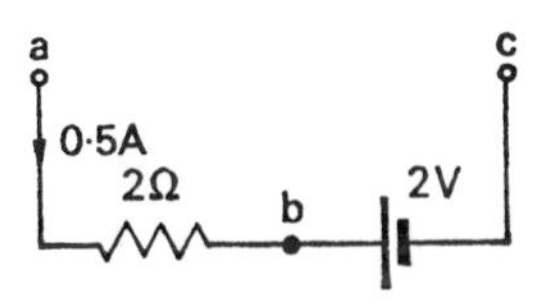

D35 In the circuit shown, the circles represent ammeters 1 to 6. If ammeter 2 reads 2.2 A and ammeter 5 reads 0.6 A, then

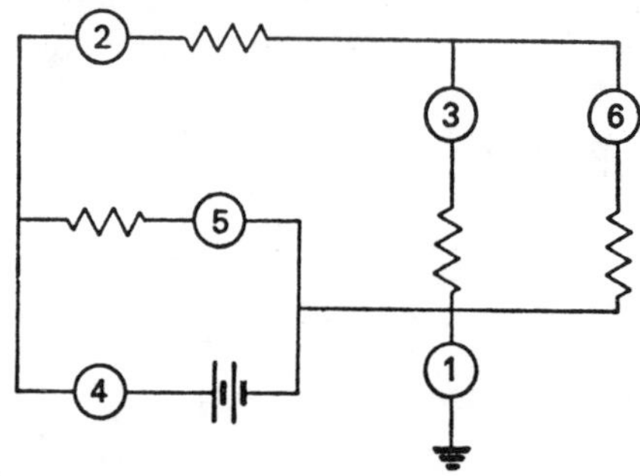

1 ammeter 4 reads 1.6 A
2 the readings of ammeters 3 and 6 total 2.2 A
3 the reading of ammeter 4 cannot be deduced
4 ammeter 1 reads zero

D36 A voltmeter of resistance 2 kΩ is connected as shown and registers 0.34 V. The ammeter registers 0.29 mA.

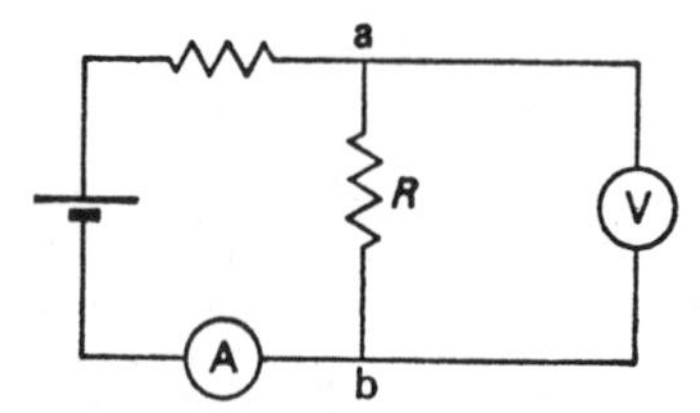

1 A current of 0.12 mA flows through R
2 The voltmeter does not register the p.d. between a and b
3 R has a resistance of more than 2 kΩ
4 The ammeter does not register the current flowing through the cell

D37 The resistance between the points K and M is

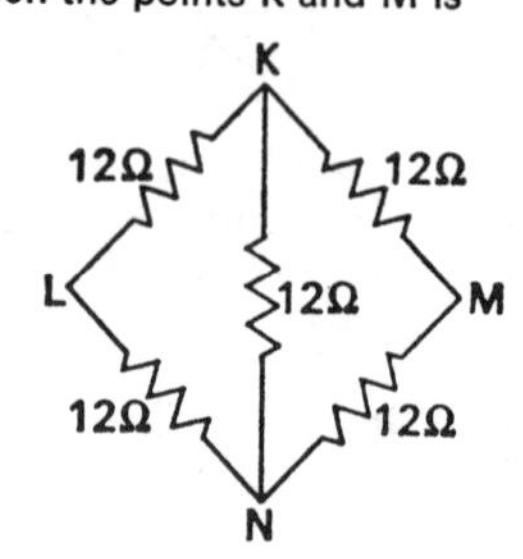

A $\frac{19}{5}\,\Omega$ **B** $\frac{25}{6}\,\Omega$ **C** $\frac{17}{4}\,\Omega$ **D** $\frac{13}{2}\,\Omega$ **E** $\frac{15}{2}\,\Omega$

D38 The resistance between the points K and N (see question **D37**) is

A 6 Ω **B** 8 Ω **C** 12 Ω **D** 16 Ω **E** 24 Ω

D39 The current I delivered by the 40 V battery in the circuit below is

A 4.0 A **B** 5.0 A **C** 6.5 A **D** 7.5 A **E** 10 A

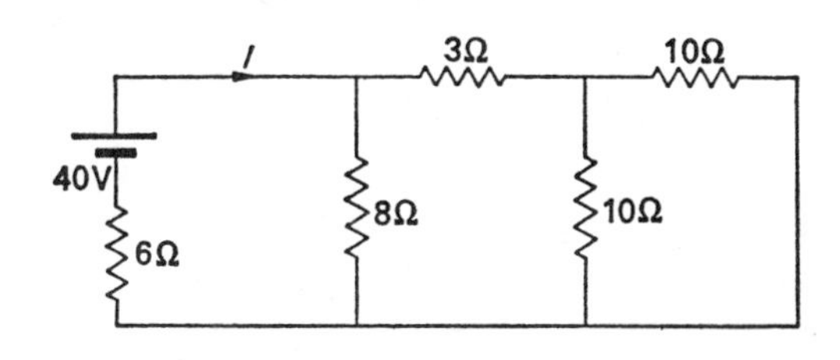

D40 In the circuit shown, P, Q, R and S are identical moving coil meters of resistance 12 ohms each.

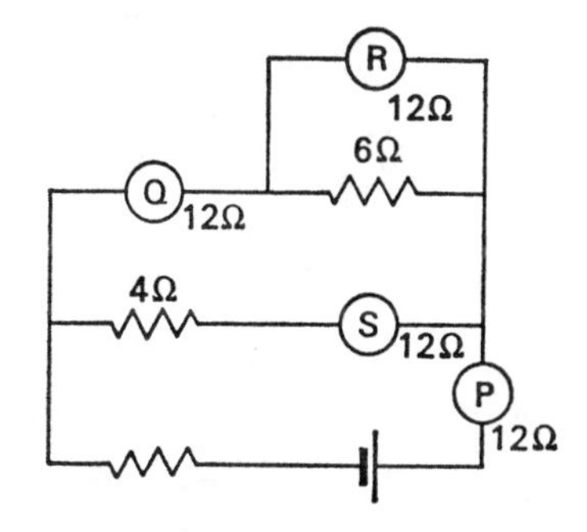

1 The readings of Q and S are the same
2 The reading of Q is three times that of R
3 The reading of P is equal to the sum of the readings of Q and S
4 The reading of P is equal to the sum of the readings of Q, R and S

D41 The network shown consists of six identical metal resistors, each of which

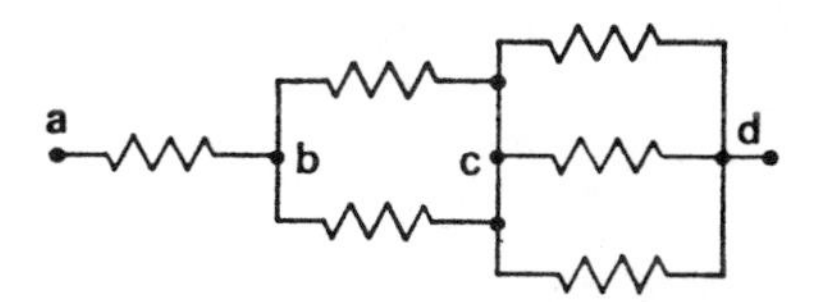

obeys Ohm's law. If $V_{ac} = 9$ V, i.e. the potential difference between a and c is 9 volts, then

1 $V_{ab} = 3 \times V_{cd}$ **2** $V_{bc} = 4$ V **3** $V_{bc} > V_{cd}$
4 not enough information is given to work out the p.d. across every resistor

D42 Using each of four resistors, each of which has a constant resistance of 12 Ω, it would be *possible* to make a composite resistor which has a value of

1 3.0 Ω **2** 20 Ω **3** 30 Ω **4** 40 Ω

D43 Each of the component resistors in the diagrams has a resistance 2 Ω. In which arrangements is the resistance between points X and Y exactly 3 Ω?

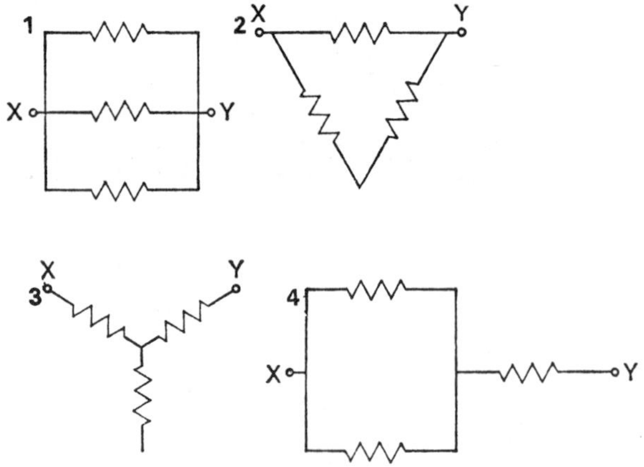

1 X Y 2 X Y

3 X Y 4 X Y

D44 A variable (sliding contact) resistor is rated 30 Ω, 1 amp. If it were used in series with a 12 V car battery to vary the brightness of a 12 V, 60 W lamp, it would suffer *no* damage from overheating
BECAUSE
the p.d. across it would never reach (30 Ω × 1A =) 30 V.

D45 If the variable resistor, rated 30 Ω, 1 amp as in question **D44**, were this time used as a potential divider across a 12 V car battery to offer a varying p.d. to a 12 V, 60 W lamp, it *would* suffer damage from overheating at one end
BECAUSE
as the dimming starts, the lamp provides a low resistance shunt to the bulk of the 30 Ω winding.

Bridge circuits

D46 For the Wheatstone bridge to be balanced, the value of R must be

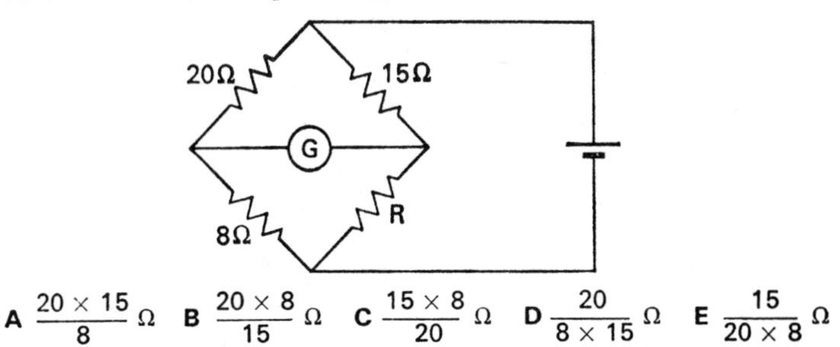

A $\frac{20 \times 15}{8}\ \Omega$ **B** $\frac{20 \times 8}{15}\ \Omega$ **C** $\frac{15 \times 8}{20}\ \Omega$ **D** $\frac{20}{8 \times 15}\ \Omega$ **E** $\frac{15}{20 \times 8}\ \Omega$

D47 Four resistors are connected as shown. A zero reading on the galvanometer, G, indicates that

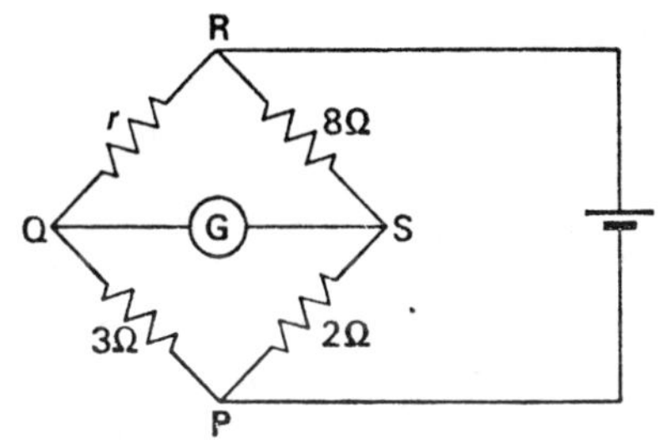

1 the p.d. between P and Q is equal to the p.d. between Q and R
2 the current in the loop PQR is equal to the current in the loop PSR
3 the unknown resistor has a value 16/3 Ω
4 the p.d. between Q and R is equal to the p.d. between S and R

D48 The galvanometer in the circuit shown has a resistance of 120 Ω. Current a divides as shown, giving currents b, c, d, e, f. In which one of the following selections are these currents arranged strictly in order of magnitude, with the biggest first?

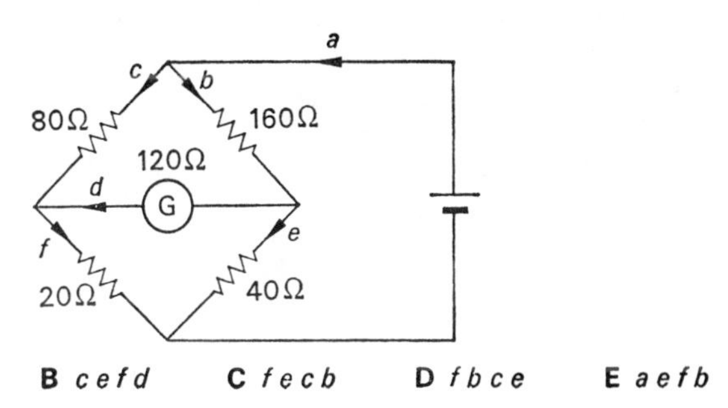

A $a\,f\,d\,b$ **B** $c\,e\,f\,d$ **C** $f\,e\,c\,b$ **D** $f\,b\,c\,e$ **E** $a\,e\,f\,b$

D49 A 50 m length of ordinary domestic triple-flex is connected as shown to the two resistance boxes having resistance R_1 and R_2, and the centre-zero galvanometer G. At the far end the three flexes, having resistances X, Y and Z, are joined together. When R_1 and R_2 are adjusted to give zero current in G,

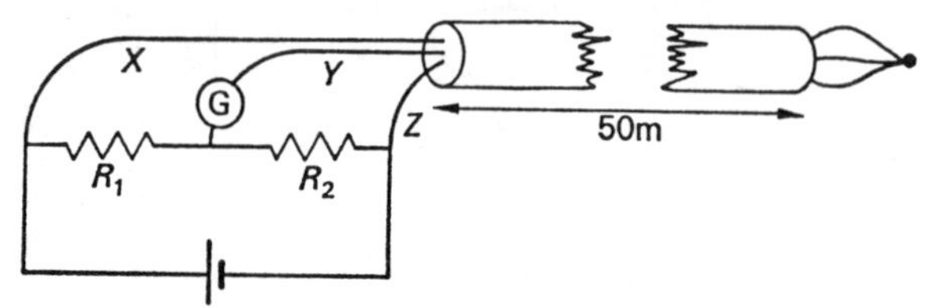

A $\frac{1}{X}+\frac{1}{Y}+\frac{1}{Z}=\frac{1}{R_1}+\frac{1}{R_2}$
B $X=R_1$ and $Y=R_2$
C $\frac{X}{Z}=\frac{R_1}{R_2}$
D $X+Y+Z=R_1+R_2$
E because of the length of flex Y, no conclusions can be drawn as to the values of X and Z

D50 The diagram shows a balanced metre bridge. F is a standard resistance; H is a pair of identical strands of constantan wire, connected in parallel with each

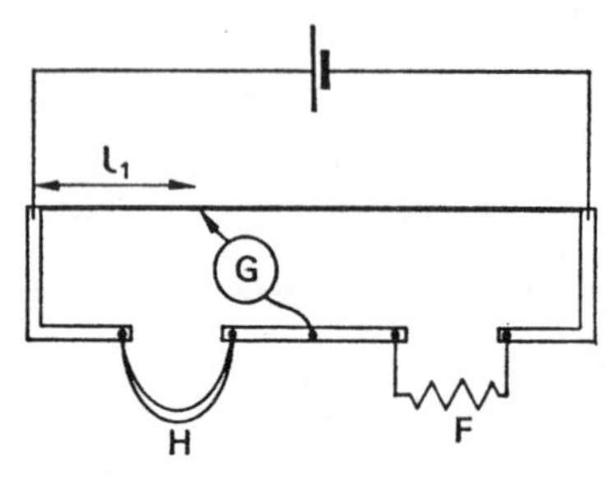

other. When one strand in H is removed, then for balance, the length l_1 must become l_2 where l_2 is

A $\frac{1}{2}l_1$ **B** l_1 (i.e. is unchanged) **C** $2l_1$

D nl_1 where n lies between $\frac{1}{2}$ and 1 **E** nl_1 where n lies between 1 and 2

Potentiometer circuits

D51 Six resistors, each of 50 Ω, are connected in a loop as shown. A 10 V battery of zero internal resistance is connected across TR. The p.d. between U and R is

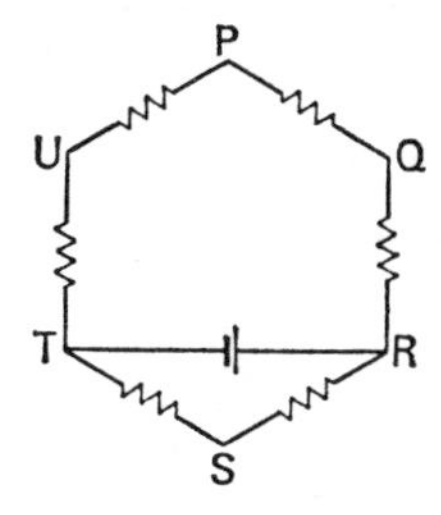

A zero **B** 2.5 V **C** 5.0 V **D** 7.5 V **E** 10 V

D52 A potentiometer is connected across ab and a balance found at 640 mm. When the potentiometer lead to b is moved to c, a balance is found at 80 mm.

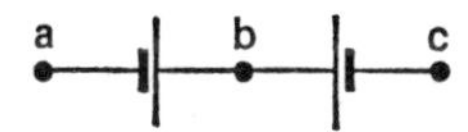

If the potentiometer is now connected across bc, a balance will be found

A at 80 mm **B** at 560 mm **C** at 640 mm **D** at 720 mm
E at 800 mm

D53 The usual simple slide-wire potentiometer circuit, as illustrated, could fairly be described as, essentially a

1 direct-reading . . .
2 voltmeter . . .
3 having a low resistance . . .
4 and a linear scale

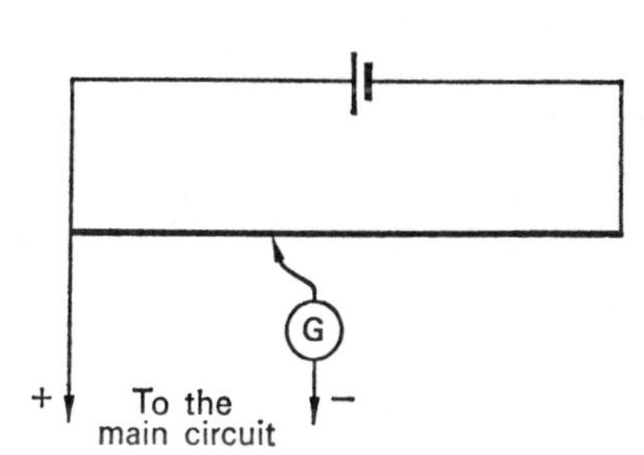

D54 A potentiometer circuit would be arranged as illustrated to

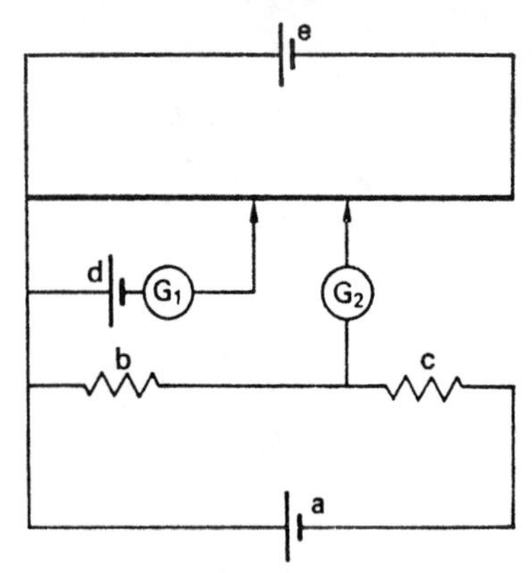

A find E_a, the e.m.f. of cell a, where $E_a > E_e$
B find the resistance of galvanometer G_1
C find the resistance of galvanometer G_2
D compare the e.m.f. of cell d with that of cell e
E calibrate the galvanometer G_2

Key: b and c : resistance boxes
a and e : cells
d : standard cell
G_1 and G_2 : centre-zero galvanometers

D55 The potentiometer circuit, at balance, matches the e.m.f. of cell P with that of cell Q, (E_P and E_Q). The cell Q, of negligible internal resistance, is now used

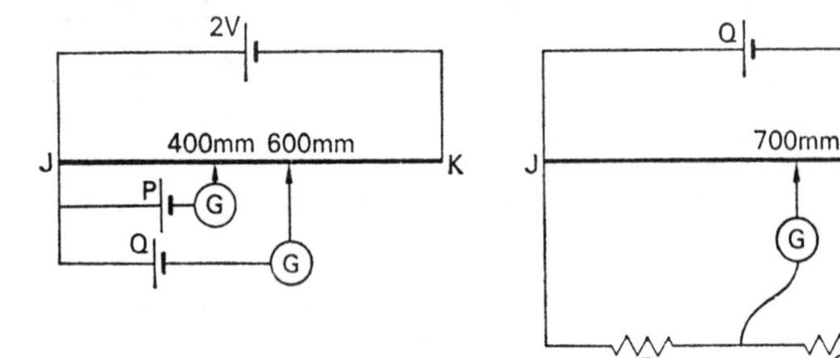

with the same metre wire, JK, to match the resistances of R and S. Then arranging the voltages V_R, V_S, E_P and E_Q in *descending* order of magnitude, we have

A E_Q E_P (V_R and V_S equal)
B E_Q E_P V_R V_S
C E_Q V_R V_S E_P
D E_Q V_R E_P V_S
E V_R E_Q E_P V_S

D56 A potentiometer circuit would be arranged as illustrated to

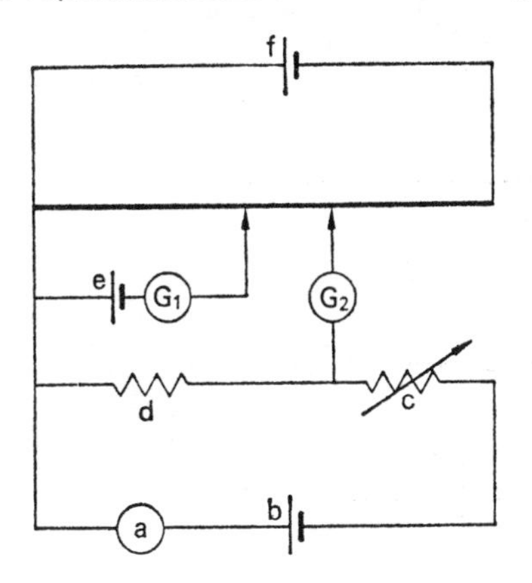

Key:
a : ammeter
c : uncalibrated sliding resistance
d : fixed standard resistance
G_1 G_2 : centre-zero galvanometers
b, f : cells
e : standard cell

A find the e.m.f. of cell b
B match the e.m.f. of cell e with that of cell f
C find the internal resistance of cell b
D calibrate the ammeter a
E match the resistance d and the internal resistance of cell e

D57 Two cells of e.m.f. 2.0 V and 1.5 V respectively are joined in a circuit with two resistors X and Y and a galvanometer, as shown. Both cells have internal resistance 1.0 Ω, and X has a resistance of 9.0 Ω. If no current flows in the galvanometer

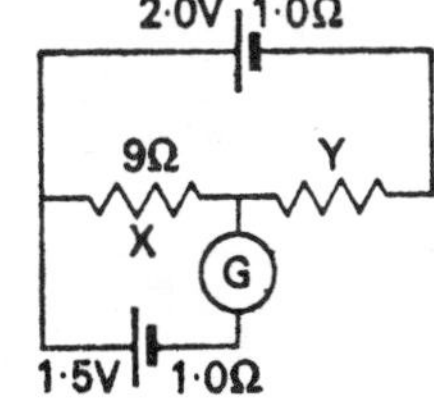

A the current in X, to the nearest mA, is 150 mA
B the p.d. across X is 1.35 V
C the p.d. across Y is 0.5 V
D the resistance of Y is 3.0 Ω
E the current in Y, to the nearest mA, is 167 mA

D58 When measuring current using a potentiometric method it is desirable that

1 the galvanometer used should have a large current sensitivity, rather than a large voltage sensitivity
2 the resistor through which the unknown current flows and across which the p.d. is measured should have the same resistance as the slide-wire
3 the e.m.f. in the potentiometer circuit should be approximately equal to the e.m.f. driving the unknown current
4 the unknown current is passed through a four-terminal resistor, the inner two terminals of which are connected to the potentiometer

D59 A potentiometer uses a driver cell of e.m.f. 2 V. The resistance of the slide wire is 10 Ω. The following resistor is needed in order to make an accurate determination of a thermoelectric e.m.f. of about 6 mV:

A 10 Ω in series with the thermocouple
B 1000 Ω in series with the driver cell
C none at all
D 600 Ω across the leads to the thermocouple
E 0.1 Ω in parallel with the driver cell

D60 The circuit shows an arrangement for calibrating the potentiometer wire JK, using a given voltage-reference zener diode, Z.

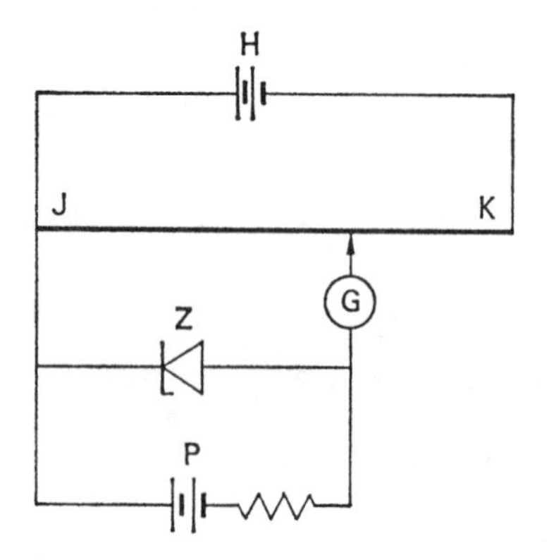

The balance length will be proportional to the e.m.f. E_p of the battery P
BECAUSE
doubling E_p doubles the current through Z.

D61 For measurement of potential difference a potentiometer is superior to a moving coil meter in the following respects:

1 it has, at balance, an infinite input resistance
2 it never needs recalibrating
3 its scale can be made a great deal longer than is feasible with the moving-coil meter
4 it is ideal for following rapid fluctuations in the observed p.d.

D62 The thermocouple gives an e.m.f. E_3 and a balance across a resistance R_3 of

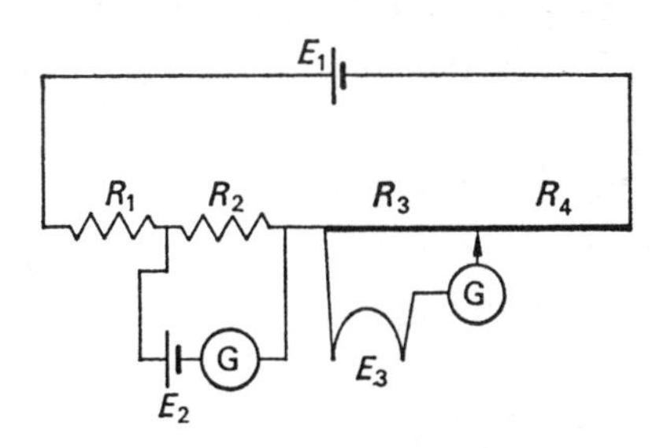

the potentiometer wire, leaving R_4 as shown. The standard cell gives an e.m.f. E_2 and a balance across R_2. Then E_3 is equal to E_2 multiplied by

A $\dfrac{R_3}{R_2 + R_3 + R_4}$ **B** $\dfrac{R_3}{R_2 + R_3}$ **C** $\dfrac{R_3}{R_2}$

D $\dfrac{R_3}{R_1 + R_2 + R_3 + R_4}$ **E** $\dfrac{R_3}{R_4}$

Thermoelectricity and electrolysis

D63 A 0.2 Ω length of copper wire is joined at both ends to a 3 Ω length of nickel wire to form a closed loop. When one junction is kept warm a steady current flows around the loop.

The fall in potential along the copper wire is identical with that along the nickel wire

BECAUSE

at the points where they touch, the two metals are at the same potential as each other.

D64 In an electrolysis experiment using a copper/copper sulphate/copper cell, a current of 1.0 A was passed for 100 minutes and the cathode gained 0.002 kg of copper. There are 10^{25} copper atoms in 1 kg of copper. The above data permit the calculation of

1 the total electric charge delivered to the cathode by the copper ions
2 the charge carried by one copper ion, Cu^{2+}
3 the ratio $\dfrac{\textit{charge}}{\textit{mass}}$ (the specific charge) for the copper ion, Cu^{2+}
4 the mean drift velocity of the copper ions in the copper sulphate solution

D65 The mass of copper liberated during an electrolytic action may, in principle, be increased by leaving all other factors constant but

1 increasing the period of time for which the action lasted
2 replacing a divalent (cuprous) electrolyte by a trivalent (cupric) electrolyte; i.e. using Cu^{3+} ions in place of Cu^{2+}
3 increasing the current
4 starting with a heavier cathode

E ELECTROSTATICS

Introduction

E1 A suitable unit for the measurement of electric field strength at a point is the

1 coulomb per metre squared **2** newton per coulomb
3 ampere metre **4** volt per metre

E2 A suitable unit for the measurement of ϵ_0 (the permittivity of vacuum) is the

A volt metre **B** coulomb per metre squared **C** coulomb per farad
D farad per volt **E** farad per metre

E3 A suitable unit for the measurement of capacitance is the

1 joule per volt squared **2** second per ohm **3** coulomb per volt
4 coulomb per joule

E4 Which of the following are vector quantities?

1 Electric charge **2** Electric potential **3** Charge density
4 Electric field strength

E5 The product *CR*, capacitance times resistance, has units

A s **B** $C\,s^{-1}$ **C** $J\,s\,C^{-1}$ **D** $J\,C^2\,s^{-1}$ **E** $J\,C^2\,s^{-2}$

Charged systems

E6 A large isolated metal sphere of radius r carries a fixed charge. A small charge is placed at a distance s from its surface. It experiences a force which is

A proportional to r **B** zero **C** proportional to $(r+s)$
D inversely proportional to $(r+s)^2$ **E** inversely proportional to s^2

E7 P and Q are two concentric metal spheres. P is charged positively and Q is earthed.

1 The charge density on Q is the same as that on P
2 The electric field inside P is zero
3 The electric field between P and Q is uniform
4 The electric field outside Q is zero

E8 P is a positively charged insulator. Q and R are in contact and made from conducting material. R is free to swing on a light insulating thread.

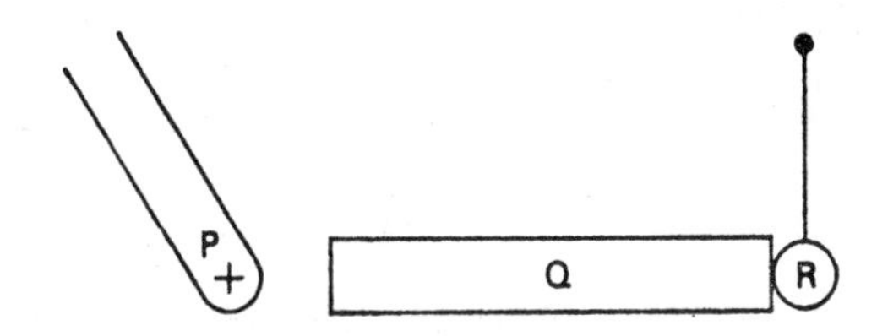

When P is brought up to Q, R swings away from Q
BECAUSE
both Q and R become negatively charged.

E9 Two metal rods P and Q on insulated stands are in contact. A negatively charged rod R is brought near Q. P and Q are now separated by moving P's stand. R is now removed.

1 P is left with a net negative charge
2 Q is left with a net positive charge
3 There is a net attractive force between P and Q
4 The negative charge on R is lower than it was initially

E10 When considering an isolated, positively charged, hollow cubical conductor,

1 the field at the surface is normal to the surface
2 the electric field strength outside the cube is greater at a corner than at the centre of a face
3 the field inside the cube is zero
4 the field outside the cube is, everywhere, directed away from the centre of the cube

Fields and forces

E11 The (circular) lines shown on the diagram are centred on the stationary charged particle. They *could* represent

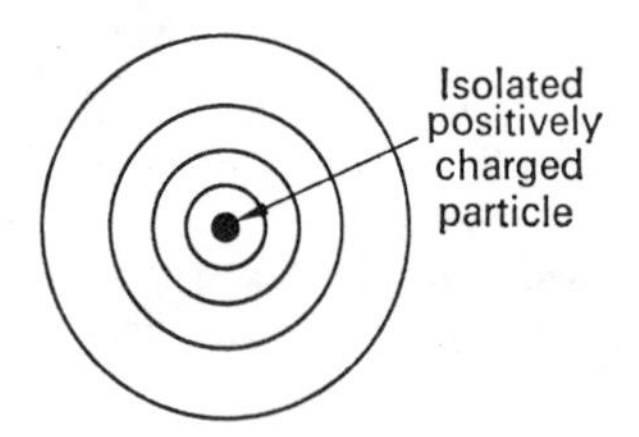

1 electric field lines **2** magnetic field lines **3** gravitational field lines
4 electric equipotential lines

E12

$$\left(\frac{1}{4\pi\epsilon_0} = 9 \times 10^9 \text{ N m}^2 \text{ C}^{-2}\right)$$

Two isolated point charges X and Y of $+2.0\ \mu$C and $-4.0\ \mu$C respectively are 6.0 m apart in a vacuum. Z is a point on the line joining X and Y, 2.0 m from X. The electric potential at Z is

A $\frac{(2 \times 10^{-6})(9 \times 10^9)}{2} + \frac{(4 \times 10^{-6})(9 \times 10^9)}{4}$ V

B $\frac{(2 \times 10^{-6})(9 \times 10^9)}{2} - \frac{(4 \times 10^{-6})(9 \times 10^9)}{4}$ V

C $\frac{(2 \times 10^{-6})(9 \times 10^9)}{2^2} + \frac{(4 \times 10^{-6})(9 \times 10^9)}{4^2}$ V

D $\frac{(2 \times 10^{-6})(9 \times 10^9)}{2^2} - \frac{(4 \times 10^{-6})(9 \times 10^9)}{4^2}$ V

E $\frac{(2^2 \times 10^{-12})(9 \times 10^9)}{2} + \frac{(4^2 \times 10^{-12})(9 \times 10^9)}{4}$ V

E13 In the previous question the electric field strength at Z has a magnitude of $x \times 10^3$ N C^{-1}, where x is

A 1.00 **B** 2.25 **C** 4.50 **D** 6.75 **E** 9.00

E14 Referring to question **E12** the force between X and Y is $y \times 10^{-3}$ N, where y is

A 0.50 **B** 1.0 **C** 2.0 **D** 12 **E** 72

E15 The two charged spheres shown are isolated conductors. As one moves from

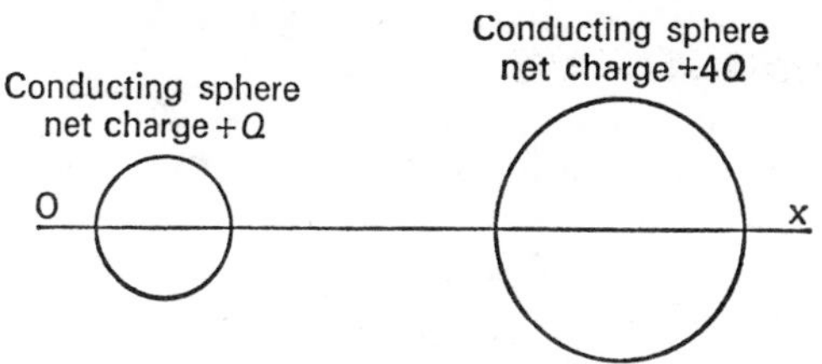

O to x along Ox, the electric potential varies as shown (approximately) in graph

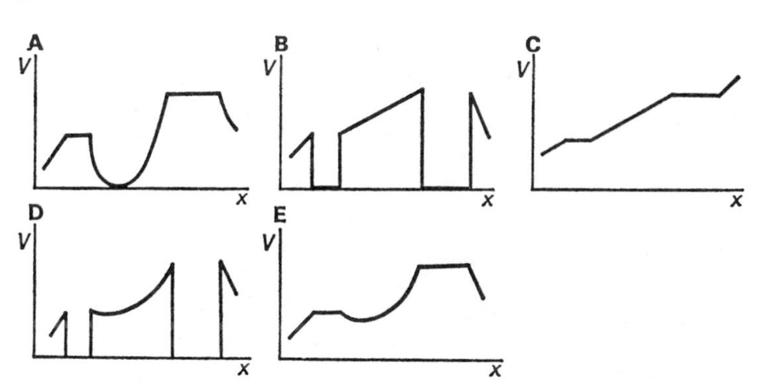

E16 Refer to the previous question. As one moves along Ox from O to x a graph showing the variation of electric field strength could *not* be represented by graphs like any of the graphs **A** to **E**
BECAUSE
on none of them does the curve drop below the axis.
(*Hint:* this would be necessary if the field was sometimes to the right and sometimes to the left)

E17 An electric dipole is held as shown in a non-uniform electric field.

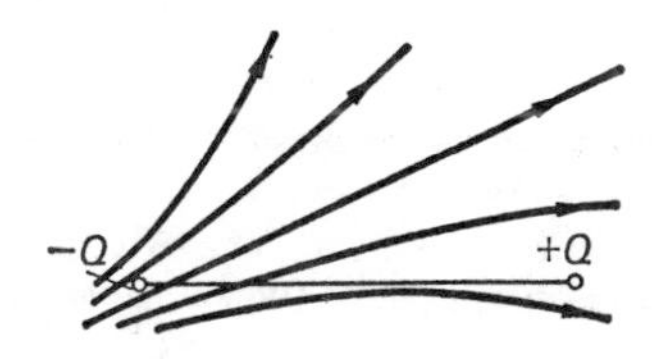

It will experience

A a torque only **B** a resultant force in the plane of the page
C a resultant force perpendicular to the plane of the page
D a torque *and* a resultant force **E** no torque or force at all

E18 Two isolated point charges are separated by 0.02 m and attract each other with a force of 40 μN. If they are moved apart a further 0.02 m then the new force between them is

A 10 μN **B** 20 μN **C** 40 μN **D** 80 μN
E calculable only if the magnitude of the two charges is known

E19 The diagram represents a singly ionised hydrogen molecule, ${}^{2}_{1}H^{+}$. The place *from which* it would be most difficult to remove the single remaining electron,

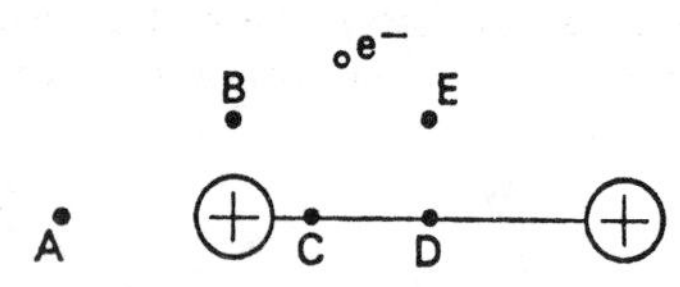

i.e. the position at which this electron is most strongly bound to the hydrogen nuclei, is

A **B** **C** **D** **E**

E20 A charged oil drop is stationary between a pair of horizontal parallel plates. If the drop carries a charge 3.2×10^{-19} C and has a mass 1.6×10^{-15} kg then the potential difference between the plates is

A 100 V **B** 500 V **C** 1000 V **D** 2000 V
E impossible to calculate from the information given

E21 In a problem you are told that an electron is liberated in an electric field of strength 4550 N C^{-1}. The specific charge e/m_e of the electron is given as 1.76×10^{11} C kg^{-1}. With no further information at all, this yields

A the mass of the electron
B the force acting on the electron
C the charge carried by the electron
D the acceleration of the electron
E nothing about the electron

Capacitors

E22 From a supply of identical capacitors rated 8 μF 250 V the minimum number required to form a composite 16 μF 1000 V capacitor is

A 2 **B** 4 **C** 8 **D** 16 **E** 32

E23 When the potential difference across a parallel-plate air capacitor is doubled, the electric field strength between the plates

A is unaltered **B** is halved **C** is doubled **D** is quadrupled
E is independent of the potential difference and consequently may have any value

E24 A 500 μF capacitor is charged at a *steady* rate of 100 μC s^{-1}. The potential difference across the capacitor will be 10 V after an interval of

A 5 s **B** 20 s **C** 25 s **D** 50 s **E** 100 s

E25 As a very small positive charge is transferred between the plates of a charged parallel-plate air capacitor, from the positively charged plate X to the negatively charged plate Y, it experiences an electrical force F which varies with distance x as shown in

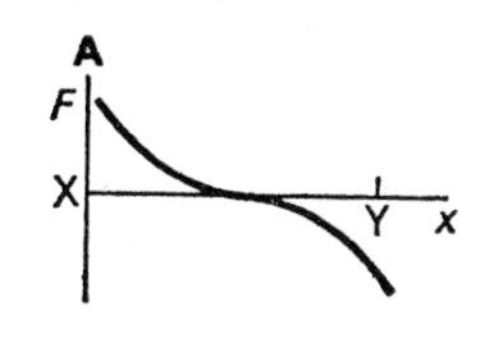

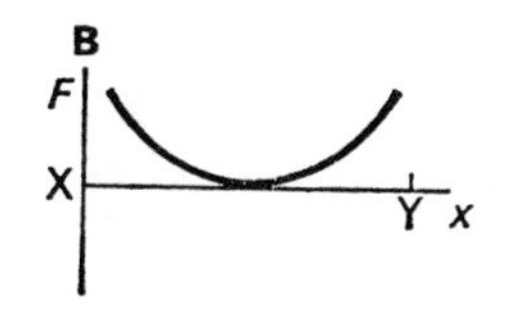

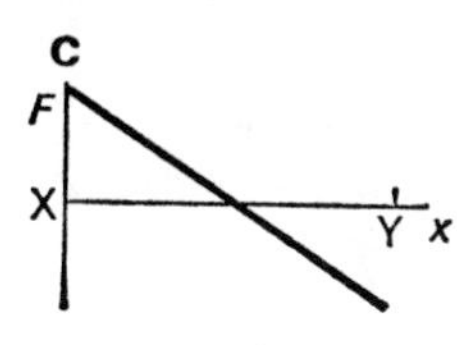

E26 A 2 μF and a 1 μF capacitor are connected in series and charged from a cell. They store *charges* P and Q respectively. When disconnected and charged separately by the same cell, they store charges R and S respectively. Arranging these charges in order of magnitude, with the biggest first and a bracket around any pair which are equal, we have

A $R\ S\ (Q\ P)$ **B** $P\ Q\ (R\ S)$ **C** $R\ (P\ Q)\ S$ **D** $(R\ P)(S\ Q)$ **E** $R\ P\ (S\ Q)$

E27 In the circuit shown, the capacitor is initially uncharged. The switch S is closed at time t_0.

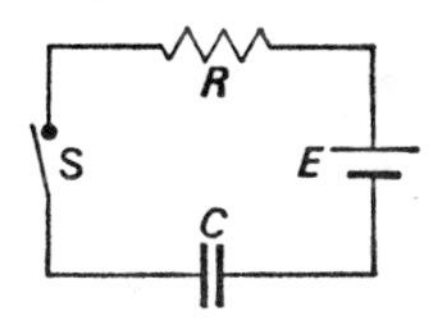

1 Immediately after t_0 the current in the circuit is determined partly by the capacitance C
2 Immediately after t_0 the current in the circuit is a maximum
3 The capacitor is fully charged after a further time t, where $t = CR$
4 The current through the resistor at any time does not depend upon the position of the resistor in this simple series circuit

E28 If the current charging a capacitor is kept constant then the potential difference V across the capacitor varies with time t as shown

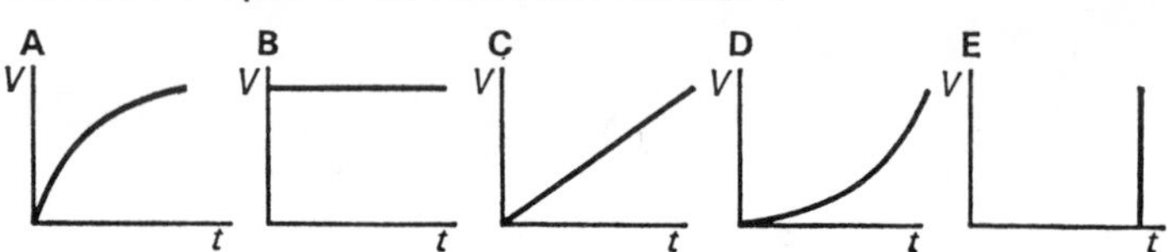

E29 A parallel-plate capacitor is fully charged by a cell and then discharged through a sensitive moving-coil meter at a high frequency f, by means of an automatic changeover switch (a vibrating reed). The average current, as shown on the meter, is

1 dependent upon f
2 independent of the resistance of the meter
3 dependent upon the distance between the plates of the capacitor
4 independent of the e.m.f. of the cell

E30 A 2 μF and a 1 μF capacitor are connected in series and charged from a cell, storing *energy* P and Q respectively. When disconnected and charged separately by the same cell, they store energy R and S respectively. Arranging these amounts of energy in order of magnitude, with the biggest first, we have

A $R\,P\,S\,Q$ **B** $P\,Q\,R\,S$ **C** $R\,P\,Q\,S$ **D** $P\,R\,S\,Q$ **E** $R\,S\,Q\,P$

E31 A gold leaf electroscope (calibrated between 500 V and 2000 V) is charged to 2000 V using a power pack. When its cap is touched by a thin wire connected to the insulated upper plate of a variable parallel-plate air capacitor, set at a capacitance of 10^{-5} μF, the leaf falls to show 500 volts. The capacitance of the electroscope is therefore

A 4×10^{-5} μF **B** 3×10^{-5} μF **C** $\frac{1}{3} \times 10^{-5}$ μF **D** $\frac{1}{4} \times 10^{-5}$ μF

E $\frac{1}{5} \times 10^{-5}$ μF

E32 Two identical parallel-plate air capacitors A and B are connected in series. The potential difference across PR is raised to V and the system isolated. When the separation of the plates of capacitor B is halved

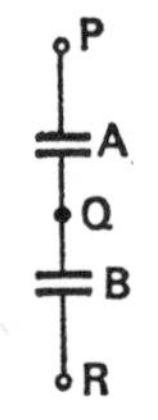

1 the charge carried by A remains the same as that carried by B
2 the potential difference between P and R falls
3 the energy of the system increases
4 the charge carried by A becomes greater than that carried by B

E33 A slab X is placed between the two parallel isolated charged plates, as shown. If E_p and E_q denote the electric field strengths at P and Q

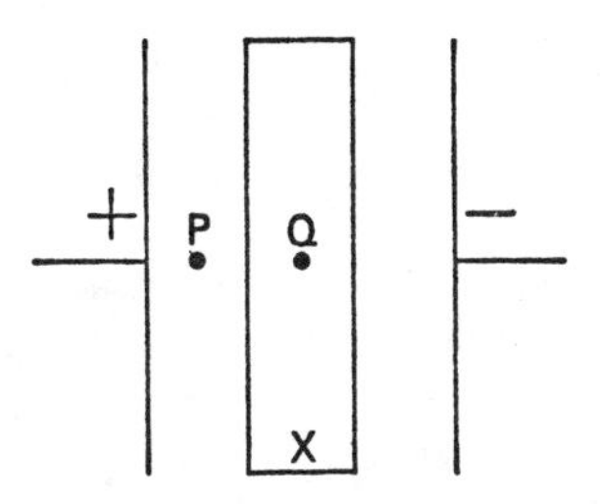

1 E_p is reduced by the presence of X if X is metallic
2 E_p is increased by the presence of X if X is a dielectric
3 E_q is in the opposite sense to E_p if X is a dielectric
4 E_q is zero if X is metallic

E34 A capacitor, of capacitance 10 μF, is discharged through a resistor of resistance 6500 Ω. The time constant of the circuit is

1 the time taken for one oscillation
2 the time taken for the current to reach its peak value
3 the time taken for the capacitor to lose 0.37 of its original charge
4 65 ms

E35 In the circuit shown G_1 and G_2 are identical centre zero galvanometers. C is a charged capacitor, and R a resistor. Immediately after opening the switch at S

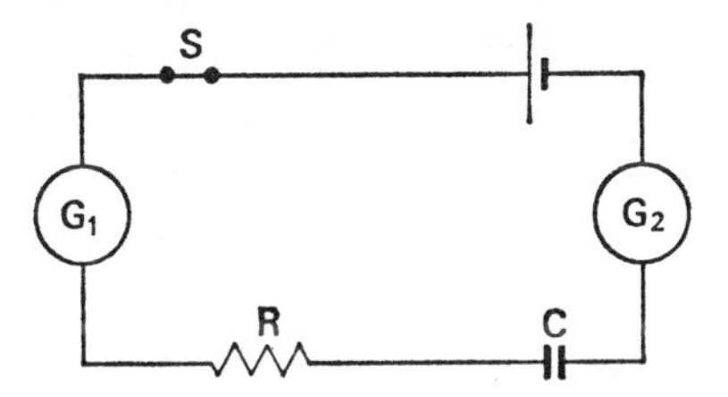

A the current through G_2 is zero
B the current through G_2 is greater than the current through G_1
C the galvanometers show kicks of equal size but in opposite directions
D the galvanometers show kicks of equal size but in the same direction
E the current through G_1 is greater than the current through G_2

F ELECTROMAGNETISM

Magnetism

F1 A piece of soft iron may be shown, in the laboratory, to experience a *net* force in

1 a uniform magnetic field
2 a converging magnetic field
3 the Earth's magnetic field
4 a diverging magnetic field

F2 A soft iron ring is to be placed so that its centre lies at X and its plane perpendicular to a uniform magnetic field. It will increase the flux density at X
BECAUSE
iron has a higher permeability than air.

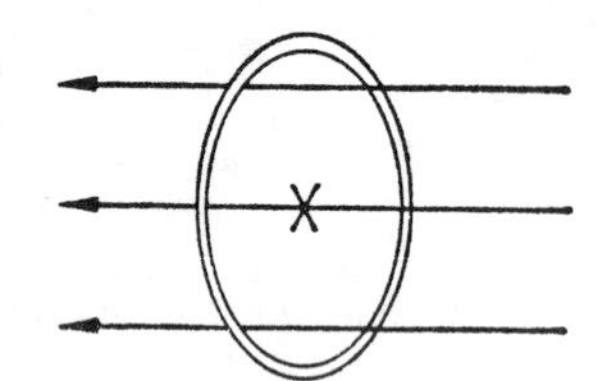

F3 If a person's right hand grips a piece of copper wire with the thumb lying along the wire in the sense of the conventional current, then his fingers curl around the wire in the sense of the magnetic field produced by the current. A similar rule relating the sense of the magnetic field to the direction of the electron flow in the wire could be devised using

1 a left hand seen in a mirror
2 a right hand seen in a mirror
3 a right hand
4 a left hand

F4 An inverse square law of distance is obeyed by

1 the electrostatic force of attraction between two charged particles
2 the force per unit length between two long straight parallel current-carrying wires in a vacuum
3 the electric field intensity outside an isolated charged sphere
4 the magnetic flux density outside a long straight current-carrying wire

Magnetic forces

F5 The mutual repulsion between two very long similar parallel wires in air is F when they each carry a certain current. If the current is doubled and the distance between the wires is trebled, then the new force between the wires is

A $\frac{2}{9}F$ **B** $\frac{4}{9}F$ **C** $\frac{2}{3}F$ **D** $\frac{4}{3}F$ **E** $6F$

F6 Four vertical conductors are shown in section at the corners of the square. They carry equal currents in the same direction. The direction of the net force

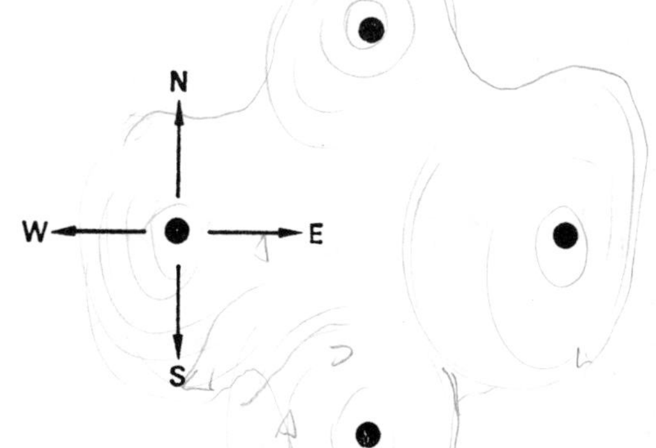

on the conductor at the far left caused by the other three (ignore the Earth's magnetic field)

A is zero **B** is to the north **C** is to the south **D** is to the west
E is to the east

F7 The supports to the pan of a beam balance are made to carry a steady d.c. as shown. If the magnet shown is externally mounted, and lies in the same plane as the supports, it will tend to

A swing the pan forward, out of the plane of the diagram
B swing the pan backward
C twist the pan clockwise as seen from above
D push the pan down
E pull the pan up

F8 A length of twin-flex carries 50 Hz a.c. to a lamp. The force of attraction, F, of the live wire for the return neutral wire varies with time, t, as shown in

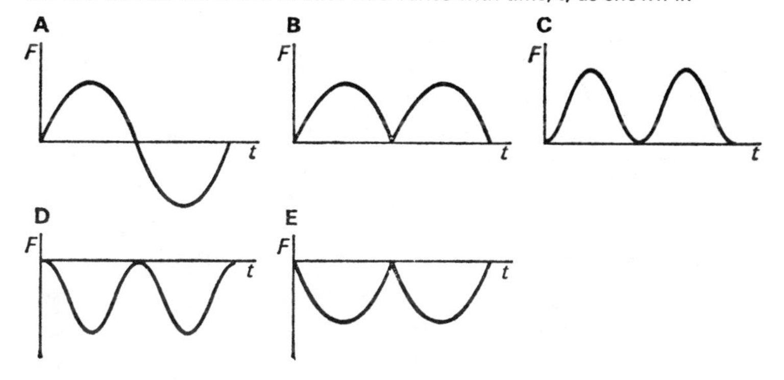

F9 Five lengths of wire, each 2.0 m long, are bent to form different rectangles and are hung in the plane of a uniform horizontal magnetic field. The one which

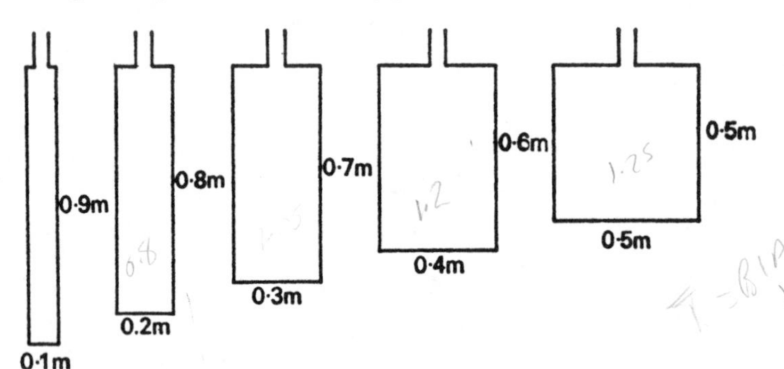

experiences the greatest couple on passing 1.0 A through each in turn, measures

A 0.9 m × 0.1 m **B** 0.8 m × 0.2 m **C** 0.7 m × 0.3 m
D 0.6 m × 0.4 m **E** 0.5 m × 0.5 m

F10 The coil PQRS is pivoted about PS, and carries a current as shown.

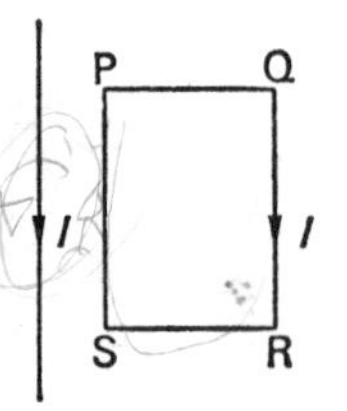

When a long wire parallel to PS carries a current in the direction shown

1 there is a net torque on the coil causing it to rotate about PS
2 the force on QR is equal and opposite to the force on PS
3 the forces on the coil tend to make it contract
4 the force on PQ is equal and opposite to the force on RS
(*Note:* neglect all forces on the coil not due to the long wire)

F11 The application of a uniform, steady, vertical magnetic field to an electron which is initially travelling horizontally through a vacuum, will produce a continuously changing

1 speed **2** radius of curvature of track **3** altitude
4 direction of travel

F12 On the application of appropriate steady magnetic fields, a high speed electron travelling horizontally through a vacuum may be given a net *initial* acceleration

A in any direction **B** only upwards, downwards or sideways
C only forwards or backwards **D** only at 90° to its path
E in any direction except forwards or backwards

F13 A positively charged ion, of a cosmic ray particle, is heading directly for the Earth's centre and if undeflected would strike the Earth at its equator. It is deflected

A not at all **B** east **C** north **D** south **E** west

F14 An electron travels due north through a vacuum in exactly the same direction as a powerful, uniform, magnetic field. It will, in principle

A be quite unaffected by the field
B be steadily accelerated, still travelling north
C be steadily decelerated, still travelling north
D follow a right-handed corkscrew path, still travelling north
E follow a left-handed corkscrew path, still travelling north

F15 An electron is accelerated to a steady high speed down the axis of a cathode ray tube by the application of a potential difference V between anode and cathode. It is then deflected by a force F caused by a transverse steady magnetic field. If the p.d. between anode and cathode were increased to $2V$, this force would assume a value of

A $F/2$ **B** F **C** $\sqrt{2}F$ **D** $2F$ **E** $4F$

Magnetic fields

F16 Suitable units for μ_0 include

A tesla **B** newton per ampere² **C** weber per metre
D kilogram ampere per metre **E** tesla metre per ampere

F17 The magnetic flux density B at a distance r from a long straight wire carrying a steady current varies with r as shown in

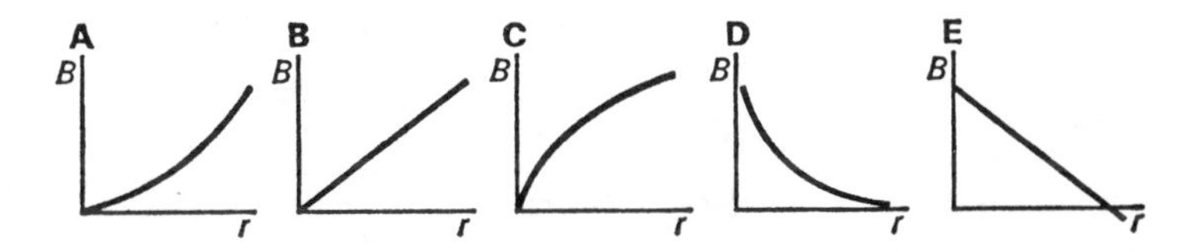

F18 Two parallel straight conductors cross a metre rule at 90° to the rule at the 2 cm and 6 cm marks. They carry currents I and $3I$ respectively, in the same direction, and produce zero magnetic flux density at the

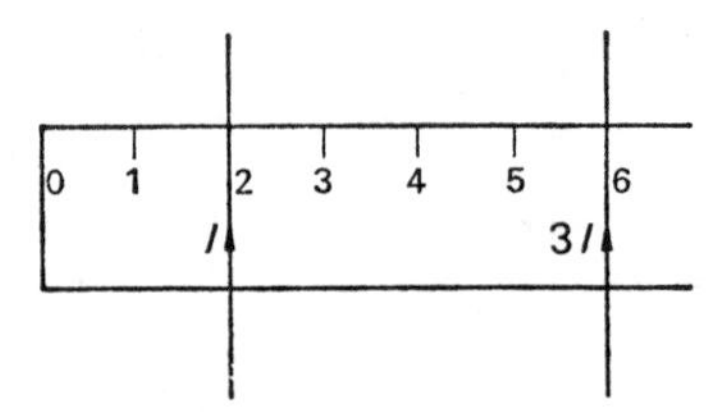

A zero mark **B** 3 cm mark **C** 5 cm mark **D** 8 cm mark **E** 10 cm mark

F19 The magnetic flux density at P, a distance s east of the 90° bend in the long straight horizontal wire illustrated, when this is carrying a current I, is

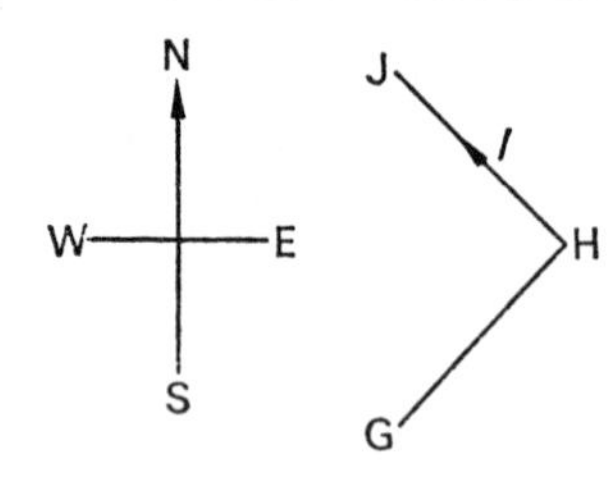

A $\mu_0 \frac{I}{2\pi s}$ **B** $\mu_0 \frac{I}{4\pi s}$ **C** $\mu_0 \frac{\sqrt{2}I}{4\pi s}$ **D** $\mu_0 \frac{3I}{4\pi s}$ **E** infinity

F20 At a point Q, vertically above the corner H of the horizontal wire GHJ in question **F19** the direction of the magnetic field caused by the current is

A east **B** north **C** west **D** up **E** down

F21 The magnetic flux density, *in vacuo*, at the centre of any square coil of one turn, measuring a by a and carrying a current I, is $\frac{KI}{a}$ where K is a constant independent

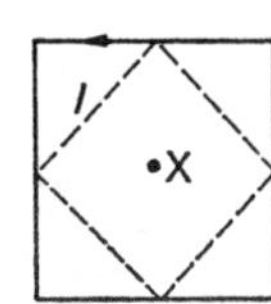

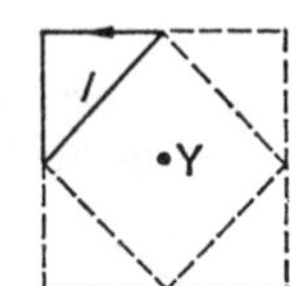

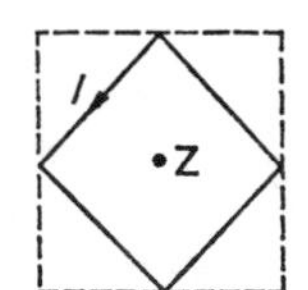

of a. The fields B_1, B_2, B_3 caused at X, Y and Z respectively, by the circuits shown, form the following relationship (ignoring direction, i.e. sign)

A $B_1 = B_3 > B_2$ **B** $B_1 > B_3 > B_2$ **C** $B_3 > B_2 > B_1$
D $B_2 > B_3 > B_1$ **E** $B_3 > B_1 > B_2$

F22 A length of wire carries a steady current. It is bent first to form a circular plane coil of one turn. The same length is now bent more sharply to give a double

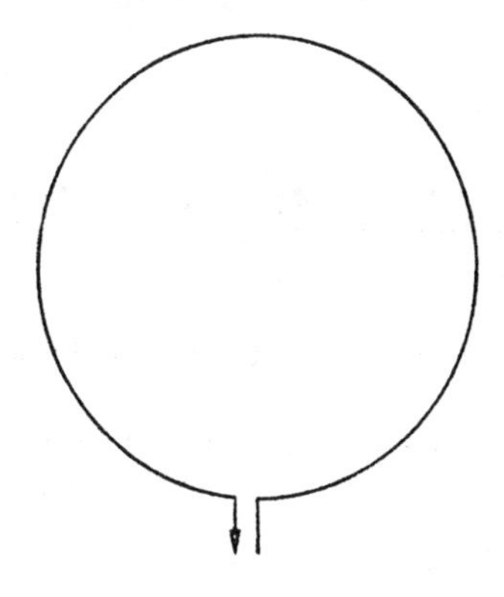

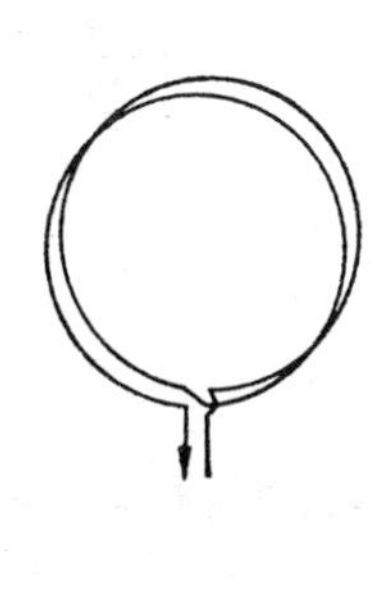

loop of smaller radius. The magnetic flux density at the centre caused by the same current is

A a quarter of its first value
B a half of its first value
C unaltered
D twice its first value
E four times its first value

F23 A long straight lead PQ is looped into a semicircle QR of radius s, and returns with RS parallel to PQ. It carries a steady current I. The magnetic flux density at O, the centre of curvature, *in vacuo*, is μ_0 times

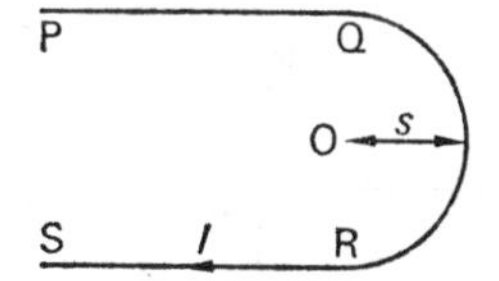

A $\frac{I}{2\pi s} + \frac{I}{2s}$ **B** $\frac{I}{4\pi s} + \frac{I}{4s}$ **C** $\frac{I}{\pi s} + \frac{I}{4s}$

D $\frac{I}{2s}$ **E** $\frac{I}{2\pi s} + \frac{I}{4s}$

F24 A straight conductor carrying d.c. is laid across the end of a long loop, also carrying d.c. In which of the areas do their magnetic fields reinforce each other?

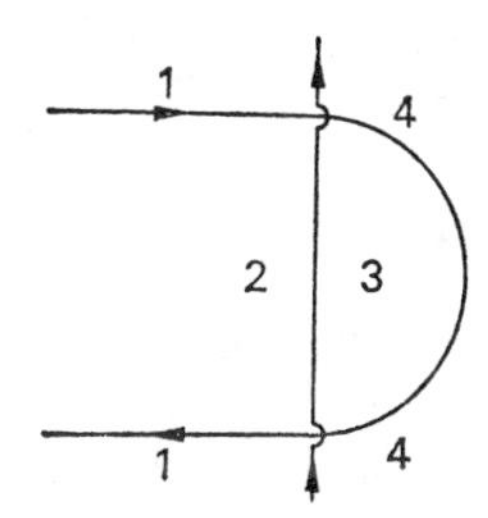

F25 Two long solenoids, of radii 20 mm and 30 mm respectively, are mounted coaxially and carry the same current. If there is zero magnetic flux inside the inner solenoid this must have x times as many turns-per-metre as the outer solenoid, where x is

A $\frac{4}{9}$ B $\frac{2}{3}$ C 1 D $\frac{3}{2}$ E $\frac{9}{4}$

F26 The magnetic flux density at the end of a very long straight air-cored solenoid carrying a direct current is x times its value at the centre of the solenoid (in each case on the axis) where x is

A 1 B $\frac{1}{\sqrt{2}}$ C $\frac{1}{2}$ D $\frac{1}{4}$ E zero

F27 The magnetic field caused by d.c. in the uniform solenoid AB, at any point X on the perpendiculars shown must have a component acting to the west

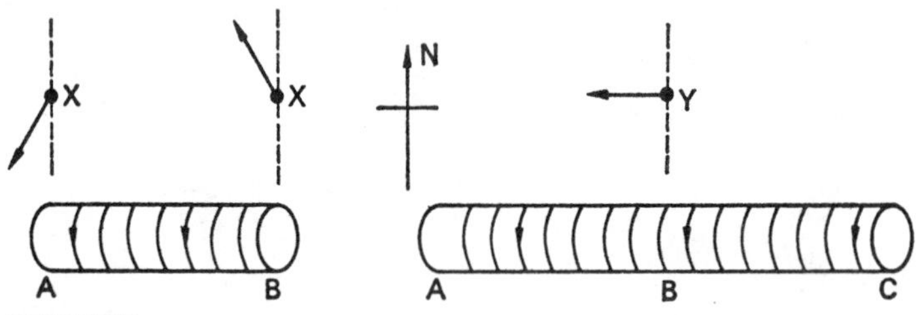

BECAUSE
its magnetic field at Y acts due west if the winding is continued to C, so making BC identical with AB.

F28 The external magnetic field associated with a *semicircular* piece of a uniform air-cored toroid ABC is symmetrical about the diameter AC

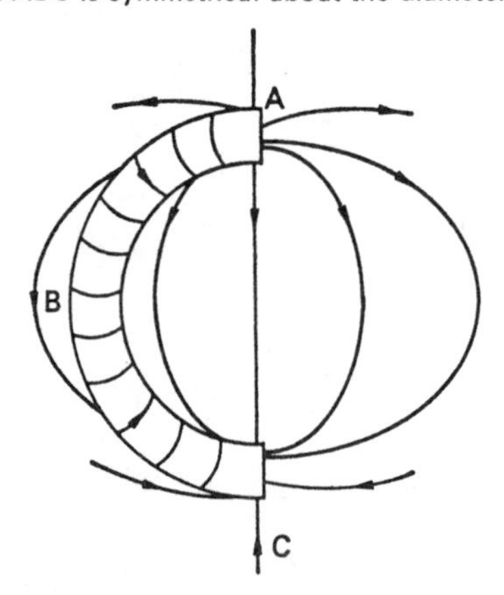

BECAUSE
the external magnetic field of a complete toroid is zero at all points.

Electromagnetic induction

F29 Suitable units for the measurement of self inductance include

1 joule ampere^{-2} **2** weber ampere^{-1} **3** ohm second **4** joule ampere

F30 The pilot of a plane carries, on board his craft, a very sensitive galvanometer connected by cable to the two tips of the metal wings of the plane, so completing a circuit through the wings. On a straight flight due north in Britain a peak current is observed because of the Earth's magnetic field

A in level flight **B** in a straight climb **C** in a straight dive
D when the co-pilot lifts the cable to get past it
E on none of these occasions

F31 A flexible copper loop is held in a horizontal plane. A magnetic dipole (i.e. a bar magnet) with its axis vertical, is dropped through the middle of the loop, from a point some way above the loop to a point some way below it. Throughout the process

1 the loop experiences a downward force
2 the loop tends to expand
3 conventional current flows in the direction shown
4 the magnet drops more slowly than it would if the loop were not present

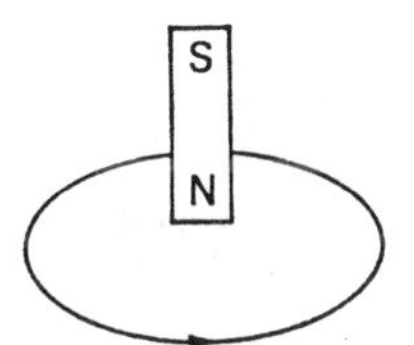

F32 A large disc of aluminium on a horizontal axle is spun clockwise, between the poles of a small horse-shoe magnet. Eddy currents will flow as shown

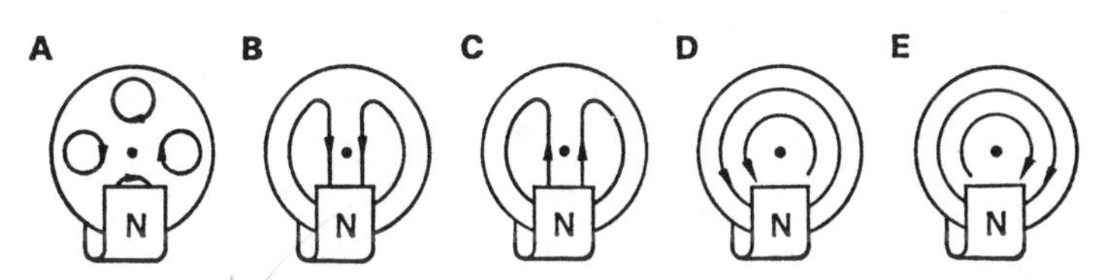

F33 A penny, with its plane vertical, is dropped alongside a long bar magnet which has its axis vertical and south pole uppermost. The free fall acceleration of the penny is altered by the presence of the magnet. It is

A decreased above and increased below the top of the magnet
B decreased above and increased below the centre of the magnet
C increased above and decreased below the top of the magnet
D increased above and decreased below the centre of the magnet
E decreased throughout its fall

F34 A current of 0.5 A is switched on in a circuit which contains a moving-coil galvanometer. The galvanometer has been damped so as to provide a reading which remains within 2% of 0.5 A as quickly as possible. Which graph shows the current reading of the galvanometer in the first second or so after switching on?

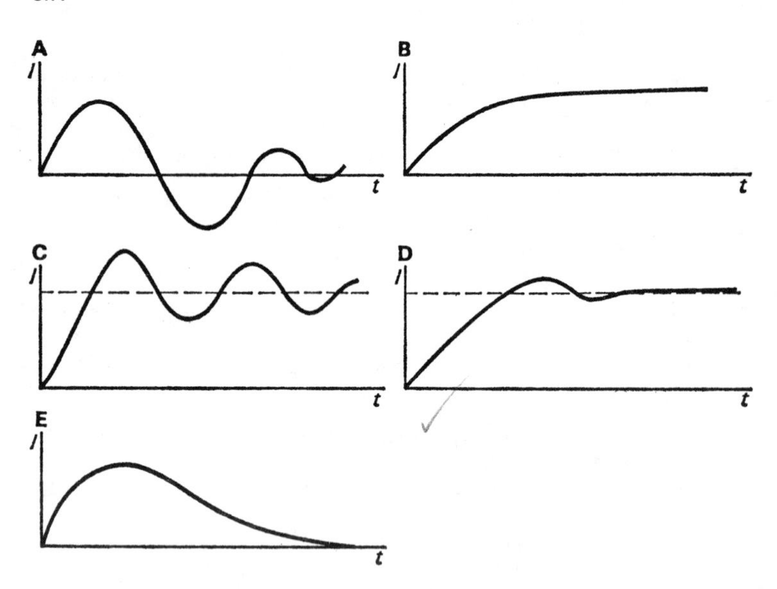

F35 A force of 10 N is required to move a conducting loop through a non-uniform magnetic field at 2 m s^{-1}. The rate of production of internal energy in the loop is

A $\frac{10}{2 \times 2}$ W **B** $\frac{10}{2}$ W **C** 10 W **D** 10×2 W **E** $\frac{10 \times 10}{2}$ W

F36 A plane circular coil starts with a uniform magnetic field *in* its plane, as shown, and is connected via a high resistance to a ballistic galvanometer. It is now

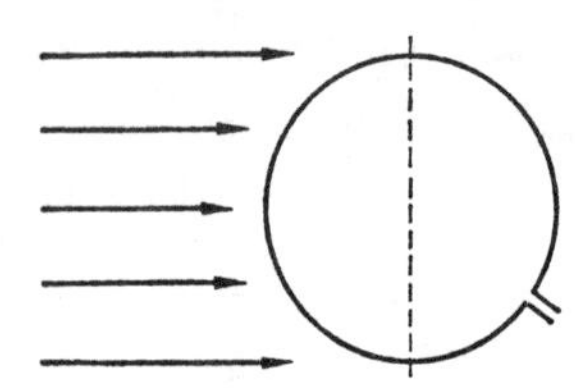

sharply spun various fractions of a revolution from rest to rest, about the diameter shown as a dashed line in the diagram. The maximum kick of the galvanometer occurs with a rotation of the coil of

A $\pi/4$ radians **B** $\pi/2$ radians **C** π radians **D** 2π radians
E $n\pi$ radians, where n is a large number

F37 A plane rectangular coil of one turn and area S is spun at a frequency n about

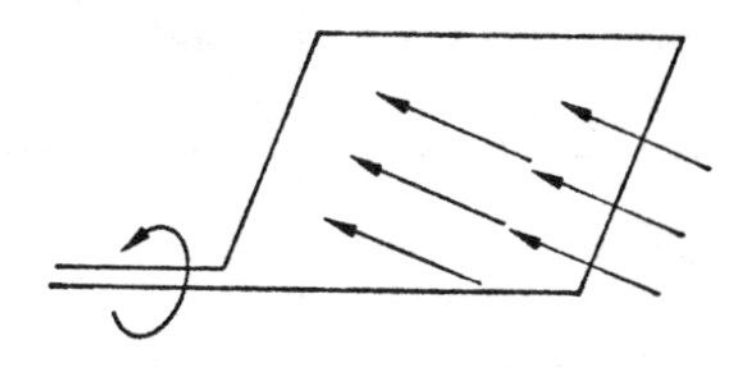

one of its sides, which is placed at 90° to a uniform magnetic field having flux density B. The *peak* e.m.f. induced in the coil is

A BSn **B** πBSn **C** $2BSn$ **D** $2\pi BSn$ **E** $4\pi BSn$

F38 A circular loop of wire is placed in a uniform magnetic field of 1.2 T that is normal to the plane of the loop. The loop shrinks from a radius of 0.2 m to a radius of 0.1 m in 0.1 s, *at a rate which generates a steady e.m.f.* This e.m.f. has a value of

A $1.2 \times \pi(0.2)^2 \times 10$ V **B** 1.2×10 V **C** 1.2×0.1 V
D $1.2 \times \pi(0.04 - 0.01) \times 10$ V **E** $1.2 \times 2\pi(0.2 - 0.1) \times 10$ V

F39 Refer again to question **F38**. In order that the induced e.m.f. should be steady, the radius r of the coil must be made to vary with time t as indicated in

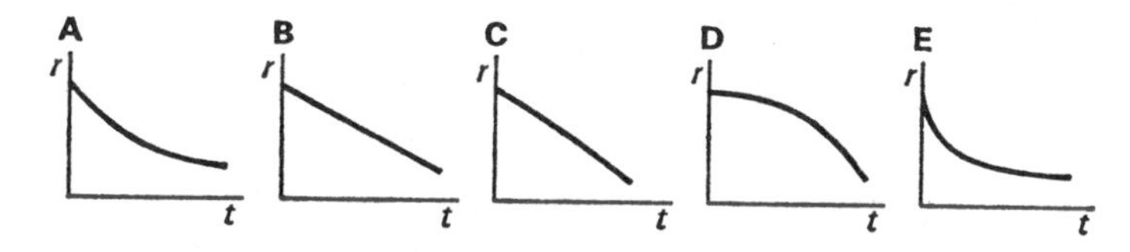

F40 The plane of a disc, radius 0.2 m, rotating at 20 revolutions per second, is at right angles to a uniform magnetic field. If the e.m.f. between the axle and the rim is 3.0 V, the flux density of the field is

A $3 \times (\pi \times 0.2^2) \times 20$ T

B $\frac{(\pi \times 0.2^2) \times 20}{3}$ T

C $\frac{(2\pi \times 0.2) \times 20}{3}$ T

D $\frac{3}{(\pi \times 0.2^2) \times 20}$ T

E $\frac{3}{20 \times 2\pi}$ T

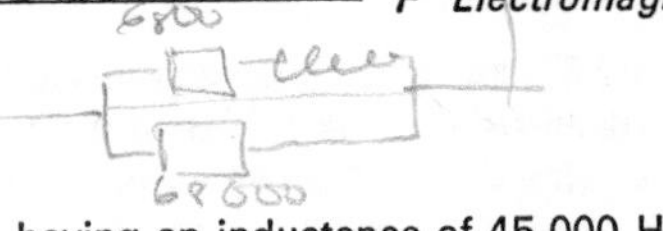

Inductance

F41 A large iron-cored inductance unit, having an inductance of 45 000 H and a resistance of 6800 Ω, is connected in parallel with a carbon resistor of 68 000 Ω. A 20 V d.c. supply is connected for about a minute to the pair, and then *very* rapidly disconnected.

1 The p.d. across the 68 000 Ω resistor jumps, initially, to about 200 V
2 The p.d. across the 68 000 Ω resistor reverses in direction as the power supply is cut off
3 Over 90% of the energy stored in the magnetic field of the inductance unit is now liberated in the 68 000 Ω resistor
4 The energy stored in this magnetic field is all liberated during the brief interval taken to disconnect the power

F42 When an inductor passes a steady current of 2 A it stores energy amounting to 10 J. With no further information we can deduce

1 the e.m.f. produced by the inductor when the current is switched off
2 the resistance of the winding
3 the time taken for the magnetic field to collapse when the current is switched off
4 the self inductance of the inductor

F43 When the switch in an inductive circuit is closed, the current increases slowly

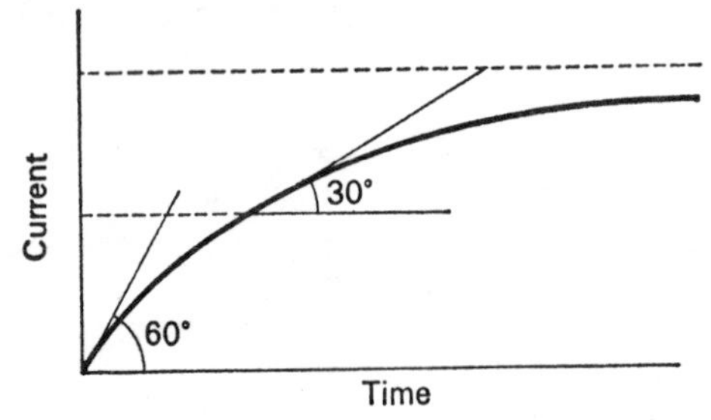

to a final value I_1. The graph shows the slope as 60° where the current is zero, and 30° where the current has reached a value I_2. Then $\dfrac{\tan 60°}{\tan 30°}$ is equal to

A $\dfrac{I_1}{I_2}$ **B** $\dfrac{I_2}{I_1 - I_2}$ **C** $\dfrac{I_1 - I_2}{I_2}$ **D** $\dfrac{I_1}{I_1 - I_2}$ **E** $\dfrac{I_2}{I_2 - I_1}$

F44 The mutual inductance between a pair of coils each of n turns is M. If a current I in the first coil is brought to zero in a time t, then the average e.m.f. induced in the second coil is

A $\dfrac{MIn}{t}$ **B** $\dfrac{MI}{t}$ **C** $\dfrac{MI}{nt}$ **D** $\dfrac{I}{Mt}$ **E** $\dfrac{It}{Mn}$

F45 A current of 100 A in one of a pair of coils is decreased steadily to zero in 3.0 s. In a nearby coil an e.m.f. of 2.0 V is induced. The mutual inductance between the two coils is

A $\frac{3}{100}$ H **B** $\frac{2 \times 3}{100}$ H **C** $\frac{2 \times 3^2}{2 \times 100}$ H **D** $\frac{100}{2 \times 3}$ H **E** $\frac{2 \times 1000}{3}$ H

F46 A long cylindrical former is wound from left to right with one layer of wire giving it n turns per unit length, with a self inductance of L_1, as in (i). If the

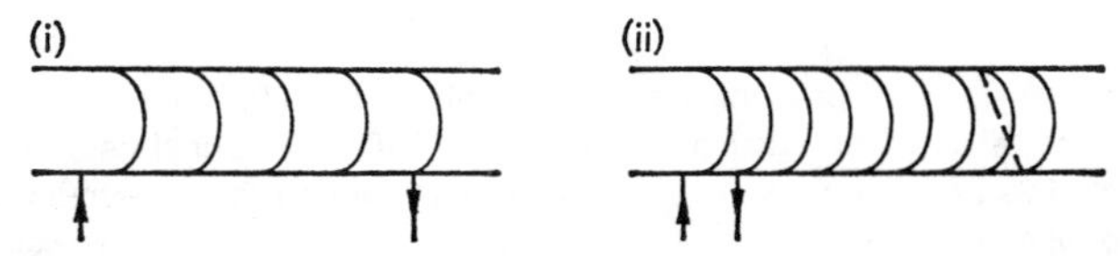

winding is now continued, in the same sense but returning from right to left, as in (ii), to give a second layer also of n turns per unit length, the self inductance becomes

A zero **B** still L_1 **C** $2L_1$ **D** $4L_1$ **E** L_1^2

F47 Two circular coils P and Q are arranged coaxially as shown, and the sign convention adopted that currents are taken as positive when they flow in the directions of the arrows.

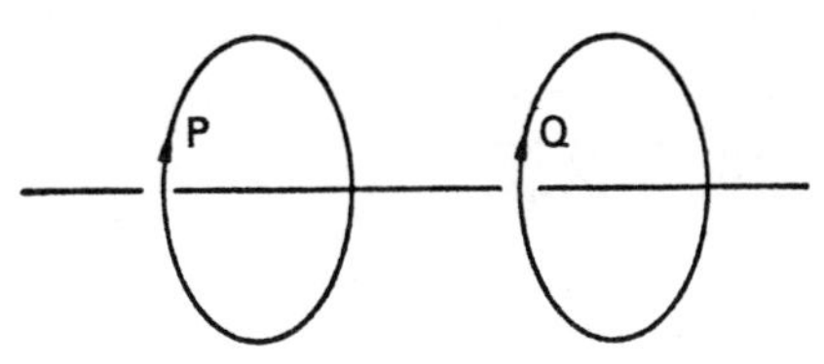

1 If P carries a steady positive current and P is moved towards Q, a positive current is induced in Q

2 If P carries a steady positive current and Q is moved towards P, a negative current is induced in Q

3 If a positive current flowing in P is switched off a negative current is induced momentarily in Q

4 If both coils carry positive currents, the coils attract one another

G ELECTRONICS AND ALTERNATING CURRENT

Alternating current in resistive circuits

G1 An a.c. supply gives 30 V r.m.s. which is fed to a pure resistance of 10 Ω. The power dissipated in this is

A 45 W **B** $45\sqrt{2}$ W **C** 90 W **D** $90\sqrt{2}$ W **E** 180 W

G2 A heavy-duty, mains, semiconductor rectifier stack is placed in series with an ordinary electric fire (which is rated 2 kW, 240 V in normal use). When connected to 240 V a.c. mains, the power consumption in the external circuit is, approximately,

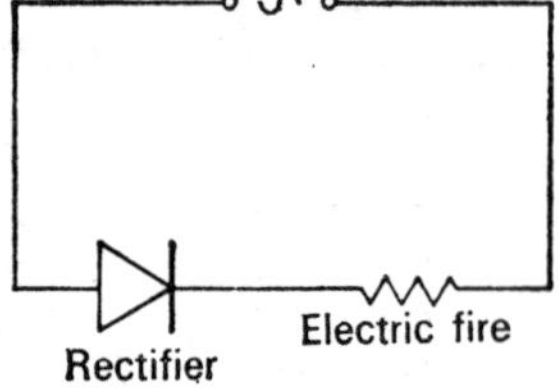

A 1 kW in the fire; zero in the rectifier
B 2 kW in the fire; zero in the rectifier
C 1 kW in the fire; 1 kW in the rectifier
D zero in both the fire and the rectifier
E zero in the fire; 2 kW in the rectifier

G3 The following could be used to measure the root mean square value of a sinusoidal alternating current in a circuit.

1 a moving-coil galvanometer
2 a moving-coil galvanometer and a rectifier
3 a cathode ray oscillograph (c.r.o.)
4 a c.r.o. plus a known resistor

G4 A sinusoidal alternating current of 5 A r.m.s. is fed, as shown, through a perfect full-wave-rectifying device to a pure resistance. If the output of the

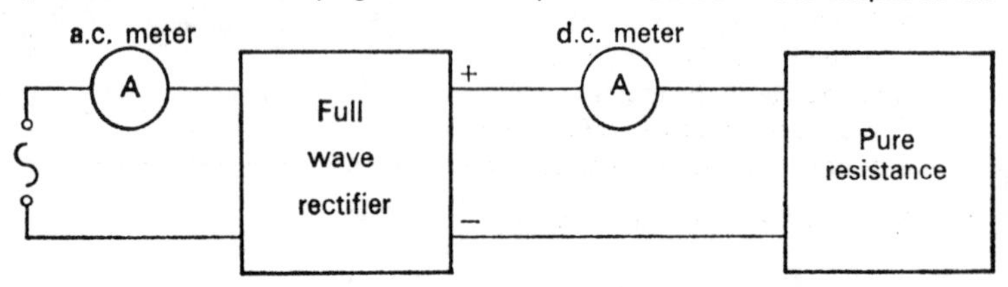

rectifying device is unsmoothed, then the moving-coil d.c. meter registers a current of

A 5 A **B** $\frac{5}{\sqrt{2}}$ A **C** $5\sqrt{2}$ A **D** $5\left(\frac{\pi}{2\sqrt{2}}\right)$ A **E** $5\left(\frac{2\sqrt{2}}{\pi}\right)$ A

G5 The ratio between the r.m.s. value and the peak value of a full wave alternating sinusoidal waveform is

A $\sqrt{2}/2$ **B** $2\sqrt{2}/\pi$ **C** $\pi/\sqrt{2}$ **D** $\sqrt{2}$ **E** $\pi/2$

Simple a.c. machines

G6 The field coils in a d.c. generator can be connected

1 in series with the armature
2 to a separate source of d.c.
3 in parallel with the armature
4 partly in series and partly in parallel with the armature

G7 A large d.c. motor has an armature resistance of 0.10 Ω and is run from the 300 V d.c. mains. The resistance required to limit the starting current to 50 A is

A 0.10 Ω in parallel with the armature
B 0.10 Ω in series with the armature
C 5.9 Ω in series with the armature
D 6.0 Ω in parallel with the armature
E 6.1 Ω in parallel with the armature

G8 A turbine is being used to drive a generator. A mechanical rate of working of 800 kW produces 250 A from the generator at 3.0 kV. The efficiency of the generator is

A 90.1% **B** 91.2% **C** 93.7% **D** 96.8% **E** 100%

G9 The circuit shows a conventional shunt-wound motor.

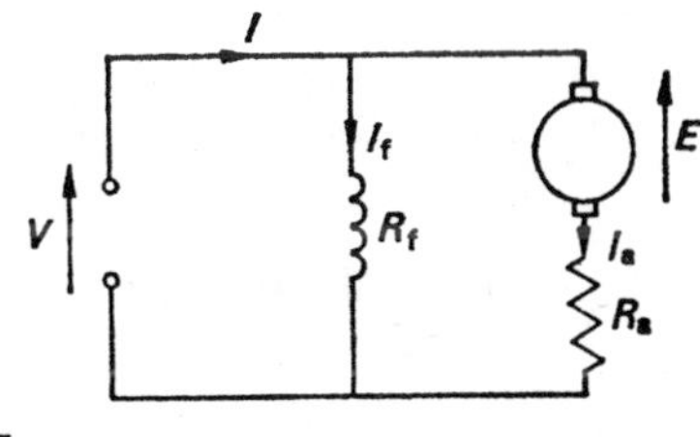

1 The back e.m.f. of the motor $E = V - I_a R_a$
2 Assuming no friction, the mechanical output of the motor $= I_a^2 R_a$
3 The electrical power $I_f^2 R_f$ does not appear as useful mechanical work
4 The efficiency of the motor is $\frac{V - E}{E} \times 100\%$

G10 Under varying load conditions, there is a greater stability of speed for a series-wound rather than for a shunt-wound d.c. motor
BECAUSE
the current in its field coils increases as the motor slows down.

G11 An ideally efficient transformer has a primary power input of 10 kW. The secondary current when the transformer is on load is 25 A. If the primary : secondary turns ratio is 8 : 1, then the potential difference applied across the primary is

A $\frac{10^4 \times 8^2}{25}$ V **B** $\frac{10^4 \times 8}{25}$ V **C** $\frac{10^4}{25}$ V **D** $\frac{10^4}{25 \times 8}$ V **E** $\frac{10^4}{25 \times 8^2}$ V

G12 Transformer cores are usually made from thin sheets of iron, neighbouring sheets being insulated from one another
BECAUSE
the eddy current losses are smaller in thin sheets than in the bulk material.

G13 The diagram represents a d.c. motor which is running with no external load. The field coils (F) and armature or rotor (A) are connected in parallel as shown

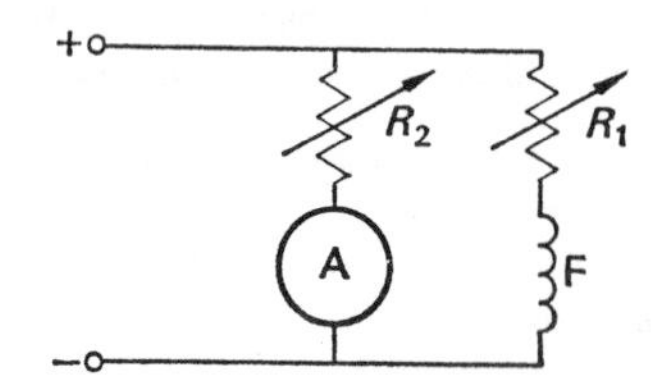

and the currents through them can be altered using variable resistors as shown. The motor will speed up if

1 the current in A is increased
2 the current in F is increased
3 the lubrication of the shaft bearings is improved
4 the current in A is decreased

G14 A d.c. motor (such as that described in the previous question) is running with no external load. The current in the armature (A) decreases when a load is applied to the motor
BECAUSE
the motor is slowed down and so the back e.m.f. in the armature coils is decreased.

G15 The figure shows the unsmoothed d.c. voltage output, V, of a low voltage unit.

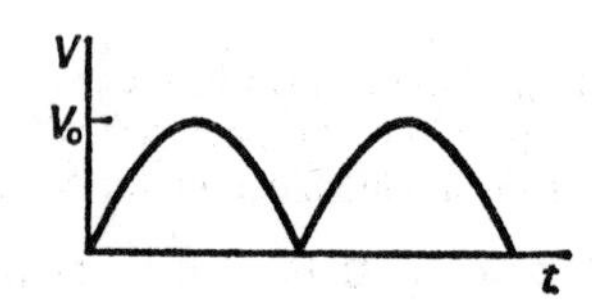

This is then fed into a 2:1 step-up transformer. Ignoring any saturation effects the output waveform is therefore

A Zero p.d. at all times

B

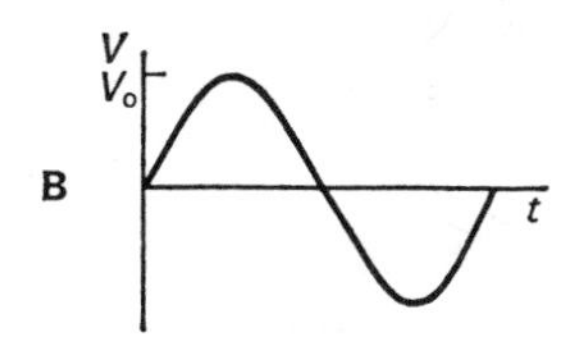

C

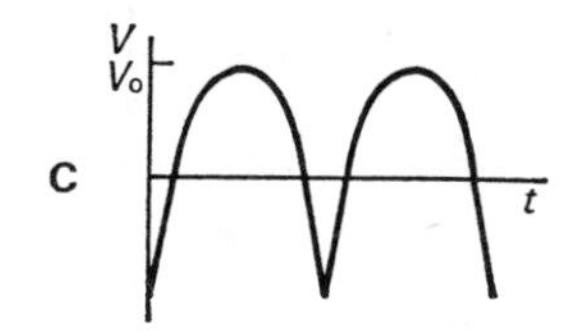

D

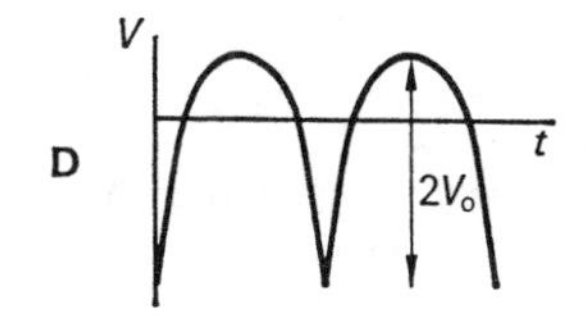

E

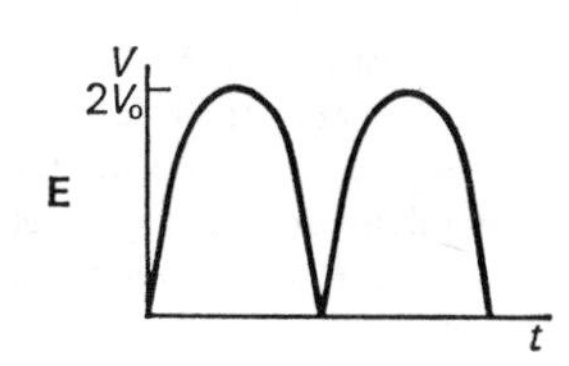

Alternating current in reactive circuits

G16 A sinusoidal alternating current flows in an inductor as shown on the graph.

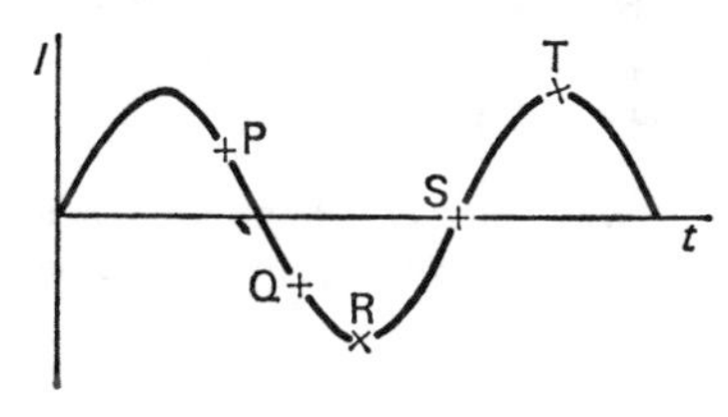

The potential difference across the inductor is a maximum at the instant indicated on the graph by the point

A P **B** Q **C** R **D** S **E** T

G17 A sinusoidal alternating current flows in a capacitor as shown in the graph used for the previous question. The potential difference across the capacitor is at a maximum at the instant indicated on the graph by the point

A P **B** Q **C** R **D** S **E** T

G18 Two identical flat coils of wire are hung freely so as to face one another.

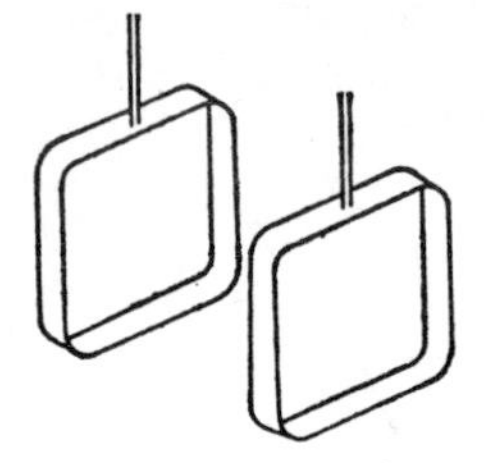

If both are fed in exactly the same way with a heavy alternating current

A they will attract each another
B they will repel each other
C they will spin in opposite directions
D they will attract, then repel each other at the frequency of the a.c.
E they will attract, then repel each other at twice the frequency of the a.c.

G19 A heavy current is passed, clockwise, through both coils of a standard mutual inductance. The small coil, starting off-centre at R, will tend to

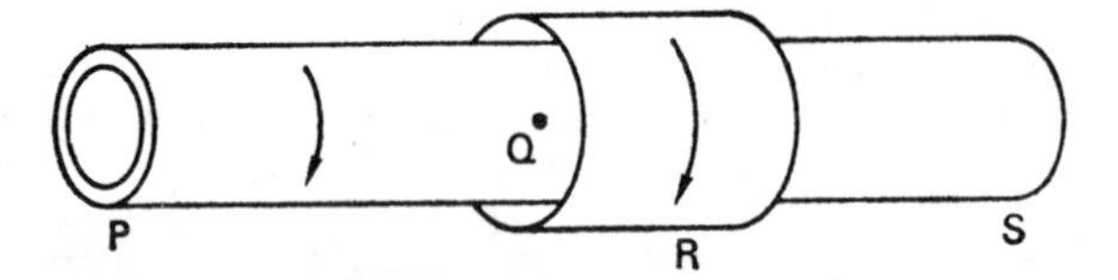

A move to the centre, Q, and stay there
B move to the end P and stay there
C move to the end S and stay there
D move right off the end at S
E move right off the end at P

G20 The phase angle between the current and the potential difference across the capacitor increases as the supply frequency decreases

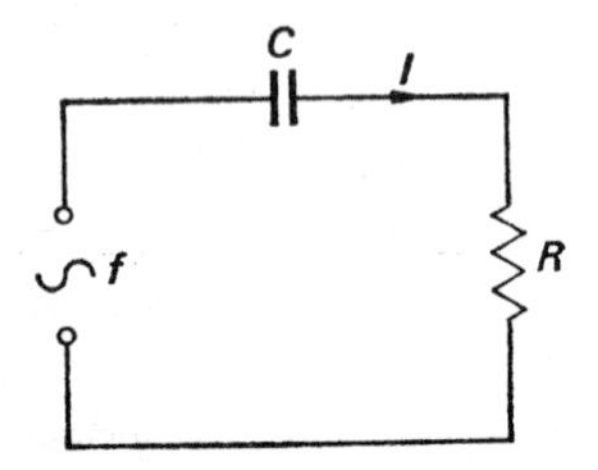

BECAUSE

the impedance of the circuit is $\sqrt{R^2 + \left(\frac{1}{2\pi fC}\right)^2}$

G21 An a.c. bicycle dynamo with negligible impedance is connected directly to a small capacitor. The a.c. current across the capacitor is I_0. The output voltage of the dynamo is doubled by doubling its speed of rotation (which incidentally doubles the frequency of the supply). The a.c. current across the capacitor is therefore now

A $8I_0$ **B** $4I_0$ **C** $2\sqrt{2}I_0$ **D** $2I_0$ **E** unchanged

G22 A coil of many turns is connected as shown to the 250 V 50 Hz supply. When

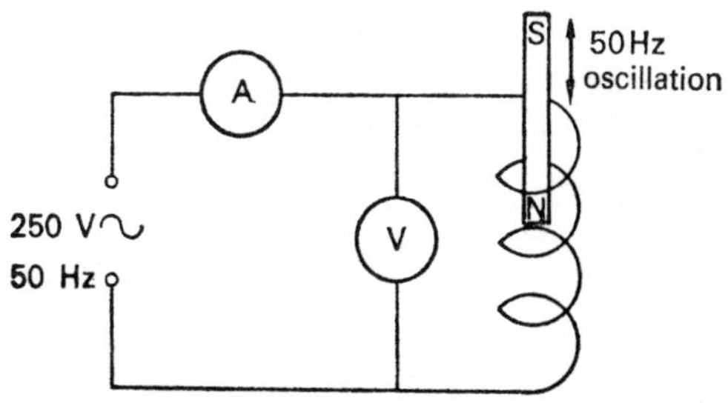

an external motor drives a powerful bar magnet in and out of the coil at 50 Hz, the reading of the ammeter

A decreases **B** increases **C** is unaltered
D may decrease or remain unaltered, depending on the phase of the drive
E may increase, decrease or remain unaltered, depending on the phase of the drive

G23 With the circuit and conditions given in the previous question, the reading of the voltmeter

A decreases **B** increases **C** is unaltered
D may decrease or remain unaltered, depending on the phase of the drive
E may increase, decrease or remain unaltered, depending on the phase of the drive

G24 A coil of many turns is connected as shown to the 250 V 50 Hz supply. When

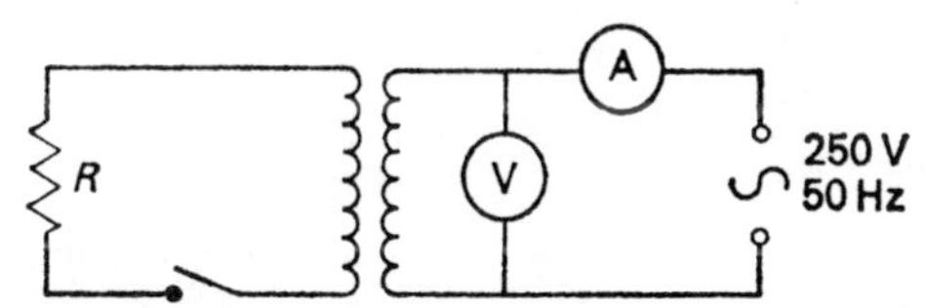

a second coil, coaxial with the first, is shorted through a low resistance R, the reading of the ammeter

A decreases and remains steady **B** increases and remains steady
C remains unaltered
D may increase or decrease depending on whether the second coil is wound clockwise or anticlockwise
E increases for a short while and then returns to its initial value

G25 With the circuit and conditions given in the previous question, the reading of the voltmeter

A decreases and remains steady
B increases and remains steady
C remains unaltered
D may increase or decrease depending on whether the second coil is wound clockwise or anticlockwise
E increases for a short while and then returns to its initial value

G26 A strong magnetic dipole (i.e. a bar magnet) is mounted as shown with its own magnetic axis horizontal. A *horizontal* circular coil of wire is arranged around

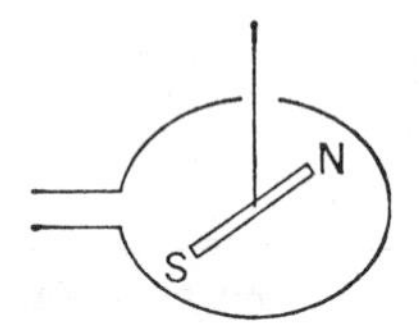

it so that the magnet lies at its centre. When the magnet is now set spinning at a steady speed about a vertical axis, the e.m.f. V between the ends of the coil varies with time t as indicated

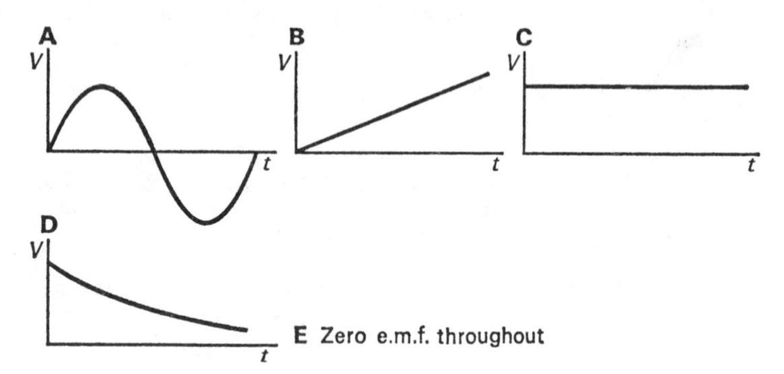

E Zero e.m.f. throughout

G27 Both circuits are designed to block the flow of current from identical, in phase, a.c. supplies.

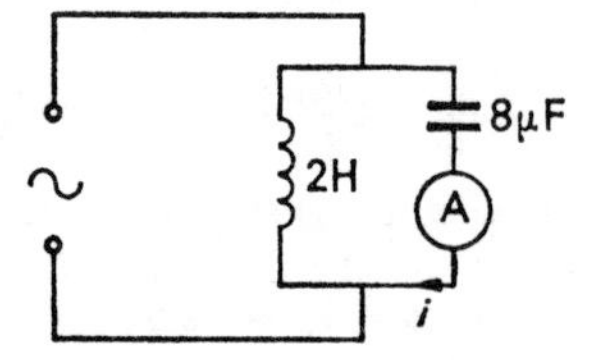

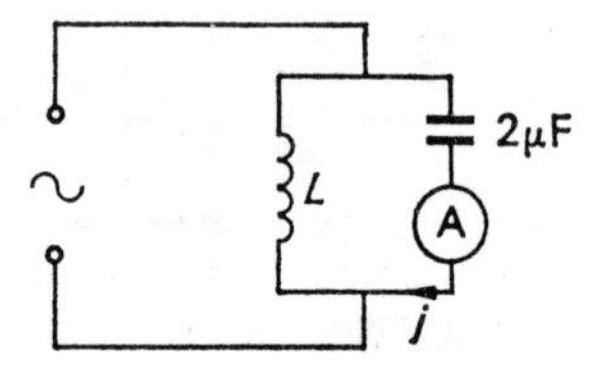

1 L must be 8H
2 $i=j$
3 The currents i and j are exactly in phase with each other
4 L must be $\frac{1}{2}$H

G28 The diagram shows an L–C blocking circuit to which a sinusoidal a.c. source

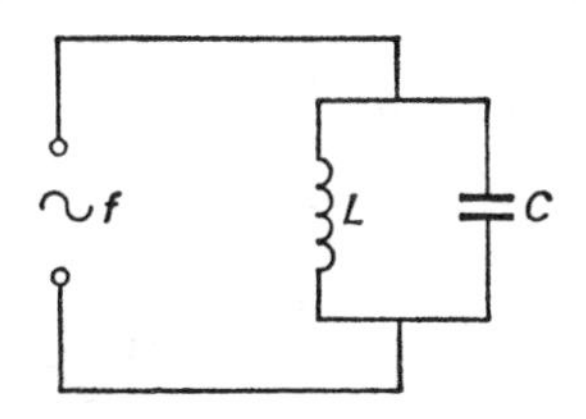

is connected. The frequency of the supply is $2\pi/\sqrt{LC}$. The energy stored by the L–C combination varies with time as shown in graph

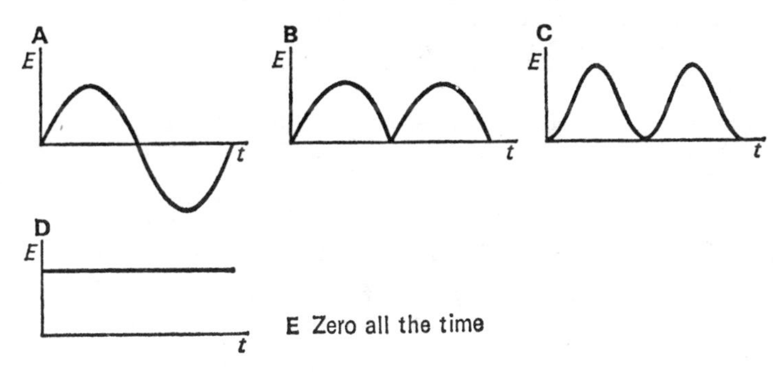

E Zero all the time

G29 The circuit can be used as an oscillator when the box P contains

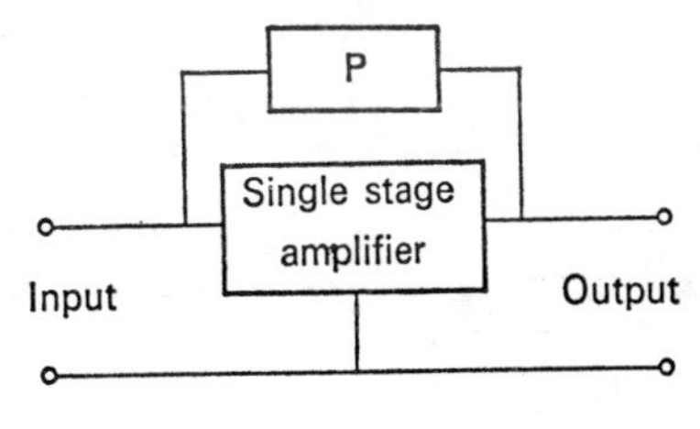

A a resistor **B** a capacitor **C** a transformer **D** an inductor
E an open circuit

G30 The sinusoidal a.c. source of *fixed voltage* varies in frequency f, and a plot of current I against f is made, This is repeated with C now in place of L. Finally both L and C, in parallel, are used.

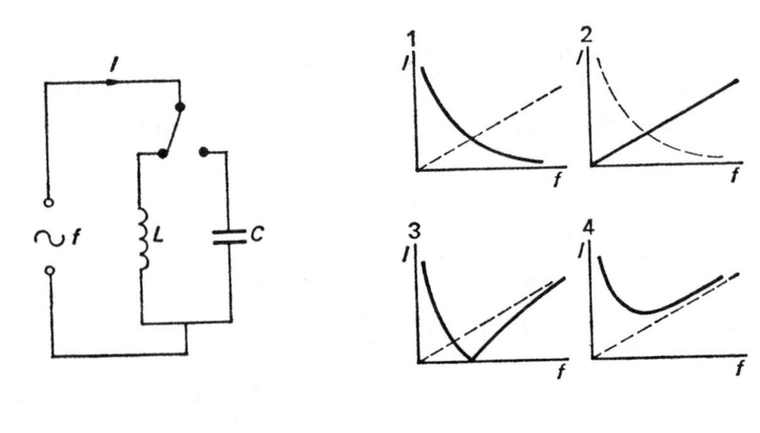

The graphs obtained, *in order*, are

A 1 2 3 **B** 1 2 4 **C** 2 1 3 **D** 2 1 4 **E** 1 1 4

NOTE In each of the next four questions (**G31–G34**) the 'square wave' input potential shown, which has a frequency of 50 Hz, is fed to one of the circuits labelled 1–4.

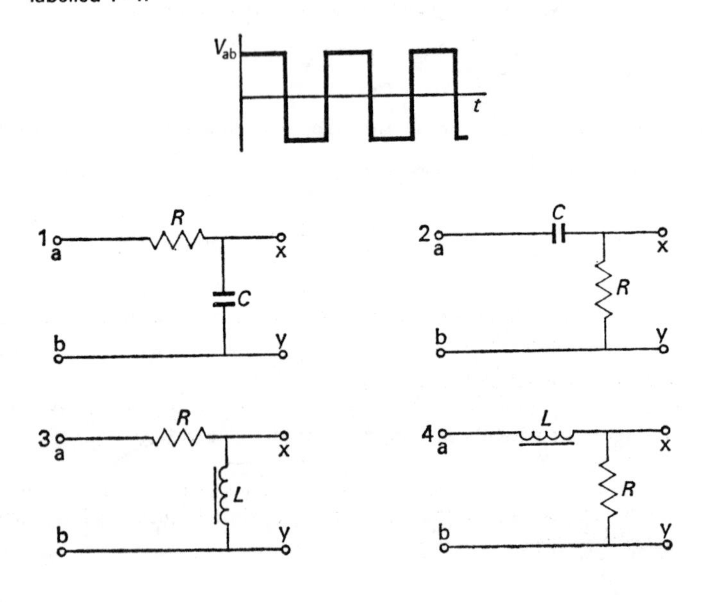

The following graphs show five possible variations of the output potential (only the shape of the curve should be considered—ignore any apparent phase relationships between the input and output potentials):

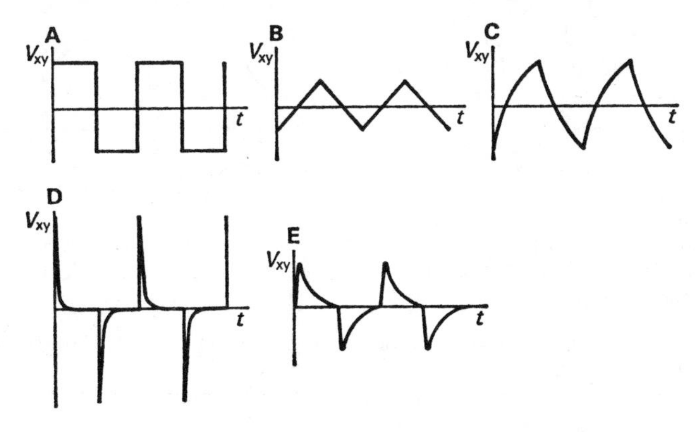

G31 In circuit 1, $R = 100\ \text{k}\Omega$, $C = 2\ \mu\text{F}$ and the frequency of the input is 50 Hz. The output potential, V_{xy}, will thus be like that shown in graph

A **B** **C** **D** **E**

G32 In circuit 2, $R = 10\ \text{k}\Omega$, $C = 0.1\ \mu\text{F}$ and the frequency of the input is 50 Hz. The output potential, V_{xy}, will thus be like that shown in graph

A **B** **C** **D** **E**

G33 In circuit 3, the output potential is like that shown in graph **E**. In order to produce **D** the ratio $\frac{L}{R}$ should be decreased

BECAUSE

this will decrease the time between the output pulses.

G34 In circuit 4, the output potential is that shown in graph **C**. In order to produce graph **B** (i.e. a sawtooth shape)

A R and L should both be increased
B L should be increased and the frequency of the input square wave increased
C R should be decreased and the frequency of the input square wave decreased
D L should be decreased and the frequency of the input square wave increased
E the amplitude of the input potential should be increased without altering its frequency

G35 The unsmoothed low voltage d.c. supply has the waveform shown, in which the r.m.s. value is 1.11 times the mean value. The meters X and Y are first

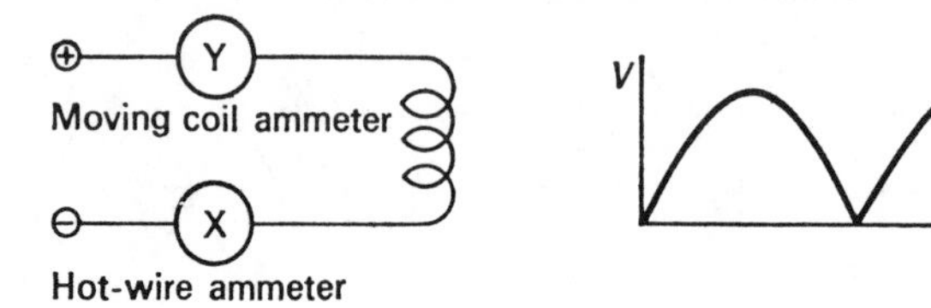

calibrated on smooth d.c., then linked in series with a coil of several hundred turns, and placed across the unsmoothed d.c. supply. When a laminated iron core is placed in the coil

A both meters register the same decrease in current
B X decreases to read the same as Y (which is unaltered)
C Y decreases to read the same as X (which is unaltered)
D X decreases more than Y
E Y decreases more than X

The cathode ray oscilloscope

G36 The diagram shows the trace made when an alternating potential difference is connected to the Y-plates of a cathode ray oscilloscope (c.r.o.), the time base being on. Various points P, Q, R, and S are indicated: the *distances* between them can be used to obtain information about the frequency, f, the period, T, and the peak to peak voltage, V, of the applied potential difference.

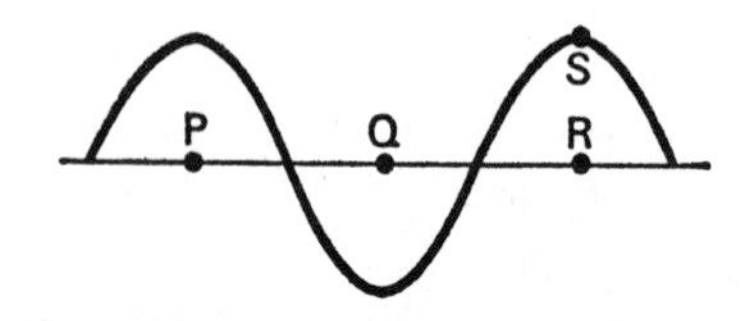

A PQ is a measure of T

B PR is a measure of f

C SR is a measure of V

D $\frac{1}{PQ}$ is a measure of T

E $\frac{1}{PR}$ is a measure of f

G37 When a p.d. of 20 V d.c. is applied to the Y-plates of a cathode ray oscilloscope, with the time base switched off, the spot of light is deflected 10 mm. If a sinusoidal alternating r.m.s. voltage of 30 V is applied to the Y-plates, the length of the trace will be

A $60\sqrt{2}$ mm **B** 60 mm **C** $30\sqrt{2}$ mm **D** 30 mm **E** $\frac{30}{\sqrt{2}}$ mm

G38 A capacitor is repeatedly discharged through a resistor across which are connected the Y-plates of a c.r.o. The trace is like that shown in the figure,

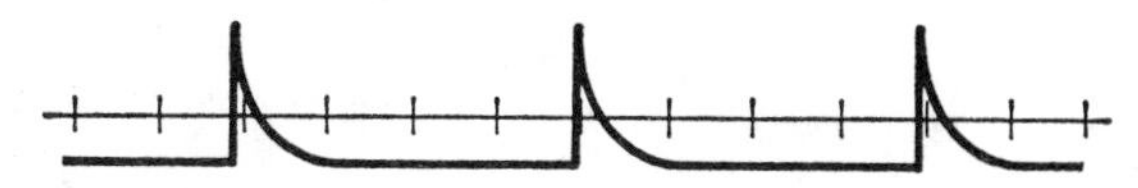

the horizontal divisions being centimetres. If the time base is calibrated and reads 100 μs mm^{-1}, then the frequency of discharge is

A 40 000 Hz **B** 4 000 Hz **C** 2 500 Hz **D** 250 Hz **E** 40 Hz

G39 The a.c. circuit illustrated is used to feed an oscilloscope with connections as shown.

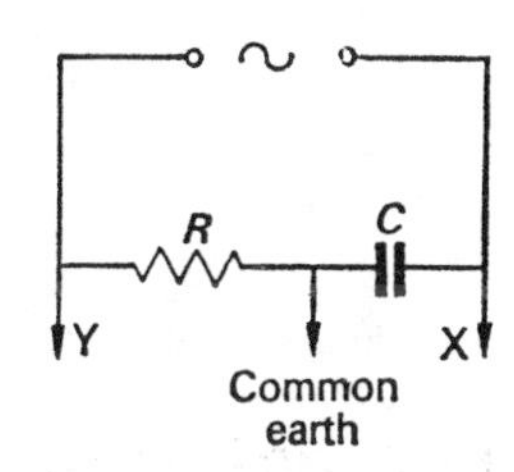

The trace on the screen would be

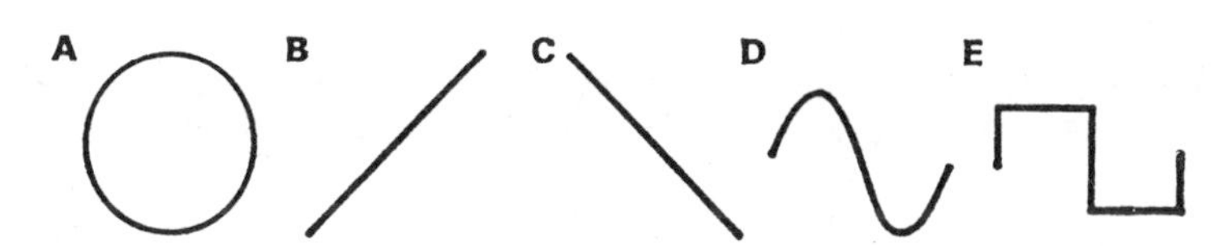

G40 A television tube of one common pattern uses an ordinary (axial) electron beam which is then deflected by a magnetic field. When the 'spot' is at the top left-hand corner of the picture, as seen from the front, the direction of the magnetic field, again as seen from the front, is

A 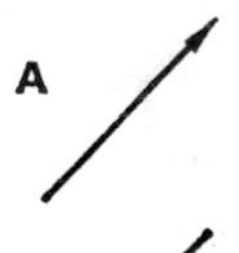

B

C directly towards the observer

D 

E directly away from the observer

G41 The following display is obtained when a sinusoidal source of unknown

frequency is connnected to the X-plates of an oscilloscope whose Y-plates are receiving a sinusoidal signal at a frequency f_0. The frequency of the unknown is

A $4f_0$ **B** $3f_0$ **C** $\frac{f_0}{2}$ **D** $\frac{f_0}{3}$ **E** $\frac{f_0}{4}$

G42 When 60 Hz signals, differing in phase by $\pi/2$ and sinusoidal in form, are applied to the X- and Y-plates of a cathode ray oscilloscope, they give a

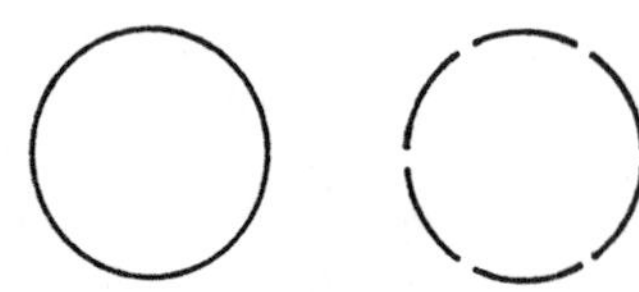

circular trace. If a signal of unknown frequency is now applied to the *grid* of the c.r.o., the circle is broken into six bright strips. This gives a value for the unknown frequency of

A 10 Hz **B** 20 Hz **C** either 10 Hz or 20 Hz **D** 180 Hz **E** 360 Hz

G43 Two square wave a.c. feeds, identical in phase, frequency and amplitude, are connected simultaneously to the X-plates and to the Y-plates of a good

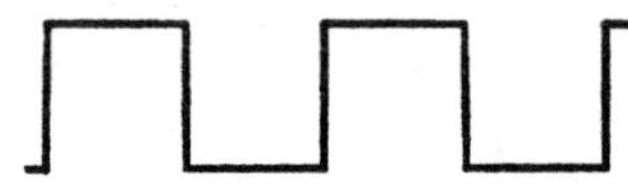

cathode ray oscilloscope. The shape of the resulting figure on the screen (ignoring variations of intensity) is

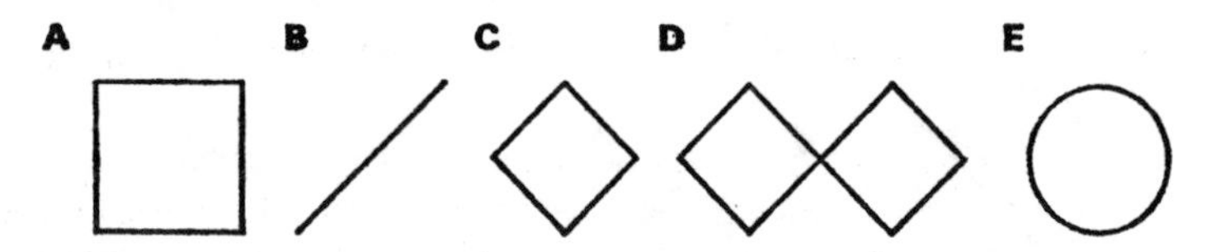

Thermionic valves

G44 For a steady heater current, the anode current I of a diode valve is linked to the anode–cathode potential difference V by the relationship $I \propto V^{3/2}$ for low values of V. As V is varied, the power dissipated as internal energy at the anode is therefore proportional to V^n where n is

A 9/4 **B** 3/2 **C** 2 **D** 5/2 **E** 3

G45 There is a lower limit to the physical size of a thermionic triode valve which can be used for anode–cathode potential differences of up to 250 V
BECAUSE
it is not possible to produce pressures within the glass envelope of below about 10^{-8} mmHg during the manufacturing process.

G46 Oxide-coated cathodes are normally used in thermionic valve tubes because they

1 will give a uniform electric field across the tube when heated by d.c.
2 can be more efficiently heated by alternating current
3 are not destroyed by positive ion bombardment
4 will produce thermionic emission at lower temperatures than metallic cathodes

G47 The curve represents the current through a thermionic diode as the anode–

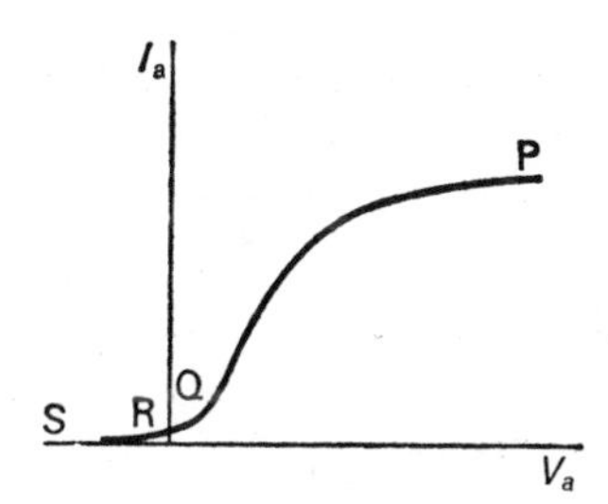

cathode potential difference is varied. Which of the following statements is *incorrect*?

A The anode current is said to saturate at P
B At saturation all the electrons escaping from the cathode cross to the anode
C The curve does not pass through the origin, i.e. the graph is correct at Q
D The current in the region of R is carried by electrons which are emitted from the anode
E No current flows in the region of S

G48 If a sinusoidal alternating potential difference is applied across XY then V, the

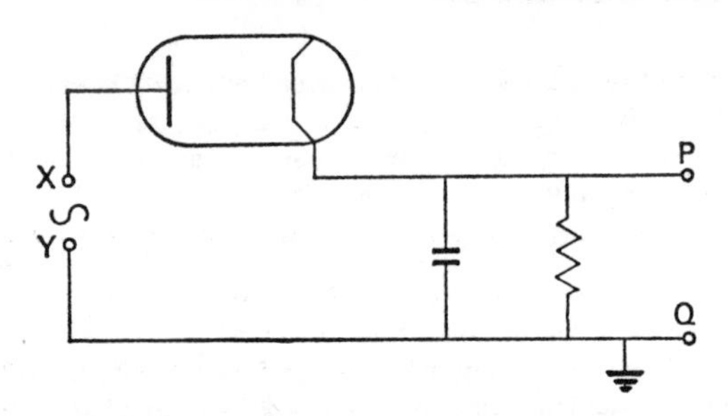

potential of P relative to Earth potential, varies with time, t, as

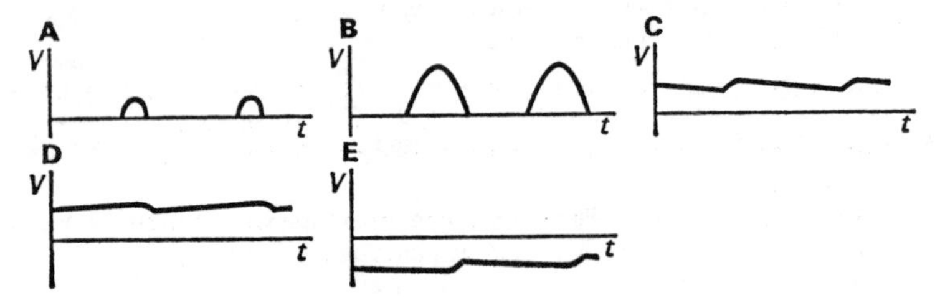

G49 The figure shows a triode valve which is being used in a circuit to demonstrate

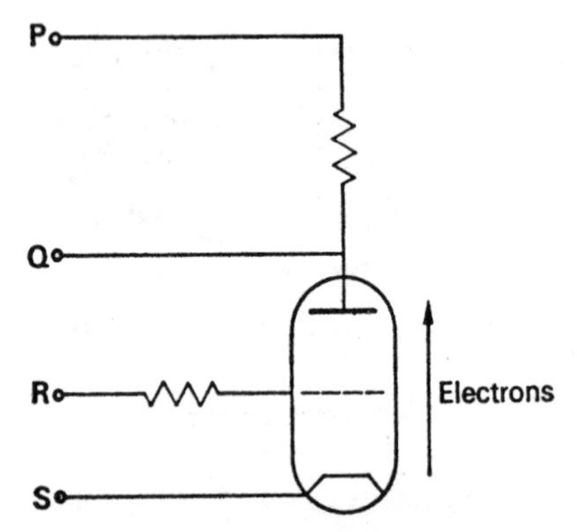

its anode characteristics. The usual voltage connections to P, Q, R and S would normally be arranged so that they were, in order of increasing potential

A PQRS **B** SRPQ **C** QPSR **D** RSQP **E** SQRP

Semiconductors

G50 The thermal energy of a metal ion in a crystal lattice at 300 K is of the order of

A 10^{-24} J **B** 10^{-20} J **C** 10^{-17} J **D** 10^{-10} J **E** 10^{-1} J

G51 Impurity atoms added to pure silicon to form an n-type semiconductor must

1 be approximately the same size as the silicon atoms so as to leave the lattice structure of the silicon crystal unaltered
2 be arranged in a regular pattern and not spread randomly through the silicon
3 each have five valence electrons and thus act as a donor impurity
4 have electrons with enough energy to escape from the surface of the semiconducting material

G52 One advantage of the transistor as compared to the thermionic triode is that the transistor can be used as a voltage amplification device at very high frequencies, whereas the vacuum triode can not. This is
BECAUSE
the distances moved by the current carriers in the transistor are very small compared to those involved in a vacuum triode.

G53 The diagrams showing energy bands for solids refer to conductors, C, insulators, I, and semiconductors, S, as indicated below in list

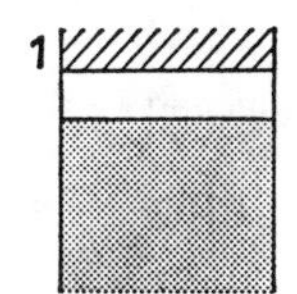

2

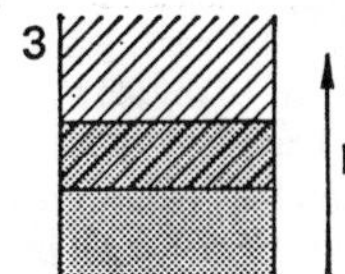

	1	2	3
A	C	I	S
B	S	I	C
C	I	S	C
D	S	C	I
E	I	C	S

G54 Hall potential differences are more difficult to demonstrate with semiconducting materials than with pure metals
BECAUSE
semiconducting materials contain fewer conduction particles per unit volume than do metals.

H ATOMIC AND NUCLEAR PHYSICS

Basic atomic behaviour

H1 Given the information in the following table:

particle	mass	charge
electron	m	$-e$
proton	$1840m$	$+e$

1 proton-volt is numerically equivalent to

A 1 electron-volt
B 1.6×10^{-19} electron-volts
C 1840 electron-volts
D $\frac{1}{1840}$ electron-volts
E some fraction of an electron-volt other than those given in **A–D**

H2 An electron and a proton travel with equal speeds and in the same direction, at 90° to a uniform magnetic field as this is switched on. They experience forces which are, initially,

A identical
B equal but in opposite directions
C in the same direction but differing by a factor of about 1840
D in opposite directions and differing by a factor of about 1840
E equal, but perpendicular to one another

H3 The energy required to ionise an atom of one of the inert gases is of the order of

A 10^{-14} J **B** 10^{-16} J **C** 10^{-18} J **D** 10^{-20} J **E** 10^{-22} J

H4 Suppose the energy required to ionise an argon atom is p, the energy required to excite an argon atom is q and the mean kinetic energy of an argon atom is r, all three energies being measured at room temperature. Placing the energies in order, with the lowest first and the biggest last, would give

A $p\,q\,r$ **B** $r\,p\,q$ **C** $q\,r\,p$ **D** $p\,r\,q$ **E** $r\,q\,p$

H5 In an *elastic* collision between a fast free electron and a stationary helium atom

A there is a net loss of kinetic energy
B very little kinetic energy can be transferred from the electron to the helium atom
C the helium atom will be excited or ionised
D the helium atom will remain at rest
E the isotopic structure of the helium atom may change

H6 Unlike electrons in a television tube, the charged raindrops from an equatorial thundercloud are not appreciably deflected, as they fall, by the externally imposed magnetic field (in this case the Earth's magnetic field). Some reasons are that

1 the raindrop carries a much smaller electric charge than the electron
2 the magnetic field is much weaker than that used to deflect the electron
3 the raindrop moves more slowly than the electron
4 the raindrop has a greater mass than the electron

H7 Suppose that a proton travelling in a vacuum with velocity v_1 at 90° to a uniform magnetic field experiences twice the force (from this field) that an alpha particle experiences when it is travelling along the same path with velocity v_2. The ratio v_1/v_2 is

A 0.5 **B** 1 **C** 2 **D** 4 **E** 8

H8 The application of a steady, uniform and vertical magnetic field to an electron which is initially travelling horizontally in a vacuum, will produce a *changing*

1 speed **2** radius of curvature of track **3** altitude **4** acceleration

H9 Given e, the charge on the electron ($\approx 10^{-19}$ C), an attempt might be made at school to measure m_e the mass of the electron ($\approx 10^{-30}$ kg) by observing the mass of a 10 000 μF capacitor (a) when both terminals are at Earth potential, and (b) when the negative terminal and outer can are still earthed, but the positive terminal is raised to +30 V.

A The method is faulty in principle, since the capacitor would carry the same total number of electrons in both cases
B The method is faulty in principle since the electron has zero rest mass
C The method is faulty in principle since this charging technique will lead to a gain in mass due to extra protons on the positive plate
D The method is faulty in principle because it does not take into account the surface charges induced on the dielectric
E The method is correct in principle but would not work because the gain in mass would be immeasurably small

Quantum effects

H10 Hydrogen gas is excited in a discharge tube and the visible radiation emitted is viewed through a spectroscope. The spectrum contains some diffuse bands of colour and one or two sharp lines.

1 The gas in the tube could *not* be pure hydrogen
2 The hydrogen in the tube contains some hydrogen atoms
3 The hydrogen in the tube is all molecular hydrogen
4 The lines are of shorter wavelength than the bands

H11 A sodium light is rated at 100 W. 10 per cent of this energy is emitted as yellow light at a frequency 5.10×10^{14} Hz. In order to estimate the number of light quanta emitted at this frequency we would also need to know

A the speed of light
B the wavelength of yellow light
C Planck's constant
D Planck's constant and the wavelength of yellow light
E the charge on a yellow light quanta

H12 The dimensions of Planck's constant, h, are

A MLT^{-2} **B** ML^2T^{-2} **C** ML^2T^{-1} **D** MLT^{-1} **E** ML^2T^{-3}

H13 A caesium photocell, with a steady potential difference of 90 V across it, is illuminated by a small bright light placed one metre away. When the same light is placed two metres away instead, the electrons crossing the photocell

A each carry one quarter of their previous energy
B each carry one quarter of their previous momentum
C are half as numerous
D are one quarter as numerous
E show no change in any respect

H14 The velocity v of electrons, each of mass m, emitted by a caesium photocell is given by the equation below

(where h = Planck's constant
ν = frequency of electromagnetic wave in use
ν_0 = lowest frequency giving emission)

A $\frac{1}{2}mv^2 = h\nu$ **B** $\frac{1}{2}mv^2 = h\nu - h\nu_0$ **C** $mv = h\nu$ **D** $mv = h\nu - h\nu_0$
E $v = h\nu$

H15 In an experiment on the photoelectric effect, the frequency of the incident radiation is varied and the potential difference needed to cut the current to

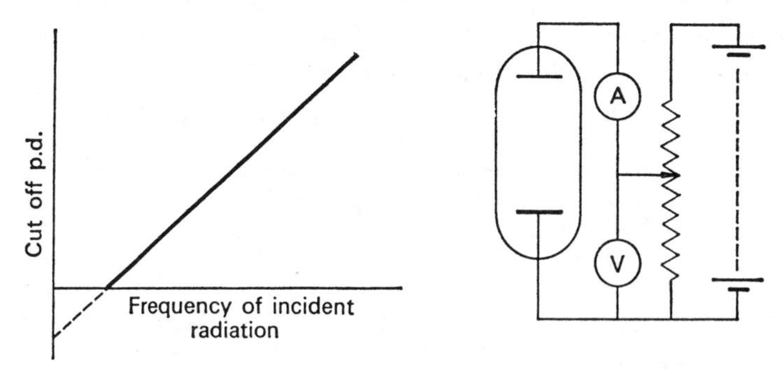

zero is noted. If the emitting electrode is now changed to one made from a different metal which also gives photoelectrons, the graph

1 cuts the p.d. axis at a different point
2 cuts the frequency axis at a different point
3 has the same slope
4 can be made to coincide with the first by altering the intensity of the incident radiation

H16 In a neon gas discharge tube the wavelength of the emitted radiation (the colour of the light) depends upon the potential difference between the terminals of the tube
BECAUSE
an ionised atom will gain more kinetic energy before making a collision when the electric field strength in the tube is high.

Atomic decay

H17 Radioactive polonium $^{214}_{84}Po$ decays by the emission of an alpha particle to

A $^{214}_{83}Bi$ **B** $^{210}_{82}Pb$ **C** $^{214}_{85}At$ **D** $^{218}_{84}Po$ **E** $^{210}_{83}Bi$

H18 A radioactive element E has atomic number *Z* and mass number *A*. It decays by alpha particle *and* gamma ray emission to

A $^{A-4}_{Z-2}E$ **B** $^{A-2}_{Z-1}E$ **C** $^{A+1}_{Z}E$ **D** $_{Z+1}{}^{A}E$ **E** $^{A+4}_{Z+2}E$

H19 $^{214}_{83}Bi$ decays by the emission of a beta particle to

A $^{214}_{84}Po$ ✓ **B** $^{213}_{84}Po$ **C** $^{210}_{82}Pb$ **D** $^{214}_{82}Pb$ **E** $^{213}_{83}Bi$

H20 Which of the following equations is or are correct?

1 $^{14}_{7}N + ^{4}_{2}He \longrightarrow ^{17}_{8}O$ + proton **2** $^{9}_{4}Be + ^{4}_{2}He \longrightarrow ^{12}_{6}C$ + neutron

3 $^{210}_{83}Bi \longrightarrow ^{210}_{84}Po$ + beta particle **4** $^{10}_{5}B$ + neutron $\longrightarrow ^{6}_{3}Li + ^{4}_{2}He$

Half life

H21 The relationship between the decay constant, λ, and the half life, $T_{\frac{1}{2}}$, of a radio-active isotope is

A $\lambda = 2T_{\frac{1}{2}}$ **B** $\lambda = \frac{1}{2}T_{\frac{1}{2}}$ **C** $\lambda = T_{\frac{1}{2}} \log_e 2$ **D** $\lambda \log_e 2 = T_{\frac{1}{2}}$
E $\lambda T_{\frac{1}{2}} = \log_e 2$

H22 The half life of a certain radioactive isotope is 3 seconds. Starting with n atoms

1 there will be $n/8$ atoms remaining after 9 seconds
2 there will be $n/16$ atoms remaining after 18 seconds
3 three-quarters of the atoms will have decayed after 6 seconds
4 there will be $n/32$ atoms remaining after 21 seconds

H23 ^{210}Bi (an isotope of the element Bismuth) has a half life of 5.0 days. The time taken for seven-eighths of a sample to decay is

A 3.4 days **B** 10 days **C** 15 days **D** 20 days **E** 34 days

H24 The number of undecayed nuclei, N, in a sample of radioactive material is

shown as a function of time in the above graph. A graph showing N (up) against the *activity* of the sample, would be like that shown in graph

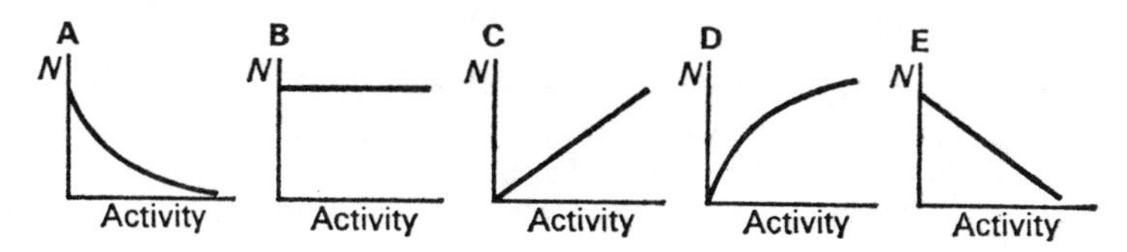

H25 An analogy has been drawn between the decay rates in a radioactive series and the flow of water through the system shown in the diagram. The tanks are

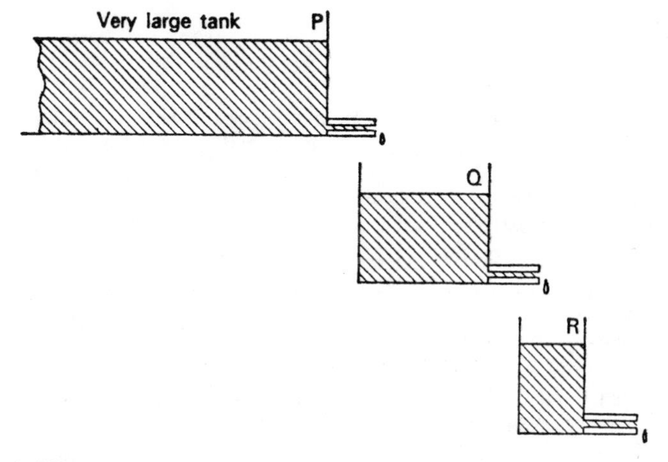

of different cross-sectional areas and are all drained by identical capillary tubes. The half-life period of the water in tank Q would be

1 a half of the time spent by a molecule of water inside Q's capillary tube
2 the time taken for the tank to lose the first half of its contents when the supply from P is cut off
3 a half of the time taken for the tank to empty itself when the supply from P is cut off
4 the time taken for the rate of loss of water by Q to be halved when the supply from P is cut off

Nuclear radiations

H26 Beta particles from a radioactive source

1 may be deflected by an electric field
2 have a velocity spectrum which is not continuous
3 can be detected in a cloud chamber
4 can be easily detected after passing through 10 mm of lead

H27 Of the three common types of radiation (alpha, beta and gamma) from radioactive sources, electric charge is carried by

A beta and gamma only
B beta only
C alpha and gamma only
D alpha only
E alpha and beta only

H28 The symbol $^{4}_{2}He$ may be used for an alpha particle
BECAUSE
it consists of 2 electrons and 4 heavier particles namely two protons and two neutrons.

H29 The radiation from a radioactive isotope is undeflected by very strong transverse magnetic fields. It also produces a small current in an ionisation chamber. The isotope is emitting

A gamma rays only
B alpha particles and gamma rays only
C beta particles only
D alpha particles and beta particles only
E alpha particles only

H30 If the interior of the base of an isolated gold leaf electroscope is painted with a material which is a powerful alpha emitter, the leaf will rise
BECAUSE
alpha particles from the base will ionise the air inside the gold leaf electroscope.

H31 A beam of mixed nuclear radiations is subjected to a strong transverse magnetic field.

A The alpha particles only are deflected
B Only the gamma rays remain undeflected, with the alpha particles and beta particles being deflected in opposite directions
C The alpha particles and gamma rays are deflected in one direction and the beta particles in another direction
D Only the beta particles are deflected
E All the radiation is deflected in the same direction

H32 The following are constituents of the nucleus of *all* atoms of oxygen:

1 electrons **2** protons **3** ions **4** neutrons

H33 The nuclear structures of hydrogen and deuterium are ^1_1H and ^2_1H respectively. Hydrogen differs from deuterium, therefore, in the following respects

1 the deuterium ion has twice the charge per unit mass of a hydrogen ion
2 each deuterium atom has two electrons in the K shell, while the hydrogen atom has only one
3 the deuterium nucleus is more massive than the hydrogen nucleus
4 the hydrogen nucleus has no net charge

H34 When beta particles with a range of energies are projected at a solid substance the back scattering observed

1 is mainly caused by interactions with nuclei in the solid
2 increases with the thickness of the target for small thicknesses
3 increases as the mass number of the target element increases
4 is detected only for certain angles of incidence

H35 The intensity of gamma radiation from a sample of ^{60}Co (an isotope of the element cobalt) is I_0. On passing through 37.5 mm of lead it is cut to $I_0/8$. The thickness of lead which would have cut it just to $I_0/2$ is

A $\frac{37.5}{4}$ mm **B** $\frac{37.5}{\log_e 4}$ mm **C** $\frac{37.5}{3}$ mm **D** $\sqrt[4]{37.5}$ mm **E** $\sqrt[3]{37.5}$ mm

The nuclear atom

H36 An atom decays in three stages by the emission of an alpha particle, a beta particle and a second beta particle. It is now once again the same *isotope* as at the beginning
BECAUSE
its atomic number has undergone no *net* change.

H37 Iron has an atomic number 26. Naturally mined iron is found to contain isotopes of mass numbers 54, 56, 57 and 58. Which of the following statements is *not* correct?

A Every atom of iron has 26 protons
B Some iron atoms have 30 neutrons
C Some iron atoms have 54 neutrons
D The isotopes may be separated in a mass spectrometer
E There are four kinds of naturally occurring iron atoms with the same chemical properties

H38 ^{132}I (an isotope of the element iodine) decays by the emission of a gamma photon of energy 3.5×10^{-13}J. To calculate the frequency of this radiation, one needs to have

1 the speed of light: 3×10^{8} m s^{-1}
2 the charge of an electron: -1.6×10^{-19} C
3 the mass of the ^{132}Iodine nucleus: 2.2×10^{-25} kg
4 the Planck constant: 6.6×10^{-34} J s

H39 A proton is fired at a nucleus. Which of the paths indicated in the diagram are possible?

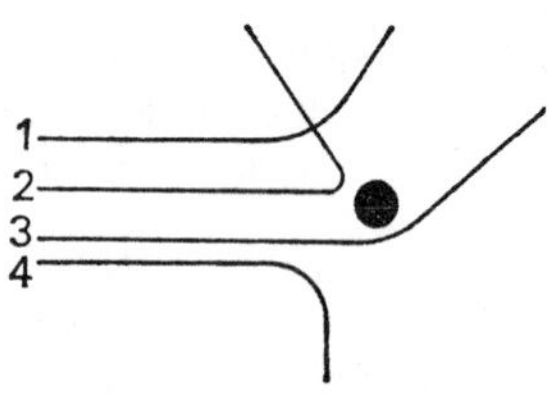

H40 There is a magnetic field acting in a plane perpendicular to this sheet of paper,

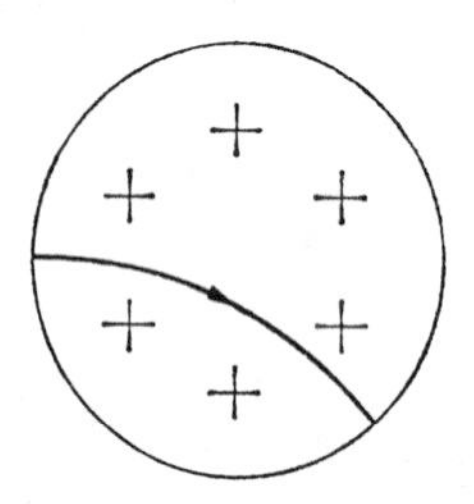

downwards into the paper. Particles in a vacuum move in the plane of the paper from left to right. The path indicated could be travelled by a

1 positively charged ion **2** neutron **3** proton **4** electron

H41 The following statements are all true. Which *one* did Rutherford consider to be supported by the result of experiments in which alpha particles were scattered by gold foil?

A The nucleus of an atom is held together by forces which are much stronger than electrical or gravitational forces
B The force of repulsion between an atomic nucleus and an alpha particle varies with distance according to an inverse square law
C Alpha particles are nuclei of helium atoms
D Atoms can exist with a series of discrete energy levels
E To disintegrate nuclei, energies of many million electron volts are needed

H42 Which of the following involves loss of electrostatic charge by the body?

1 fluorescence **2** gamma ray emission **3** X-ray emission
4 photoelectric emission

H43 The diagrams illustrate symbolically the arrival and/or emission of an electromagnetic wave or electron. The place of origin, or arrival, is shown as the nucleus or as the outer part of the atom. Which diagram illustrates beta emission?

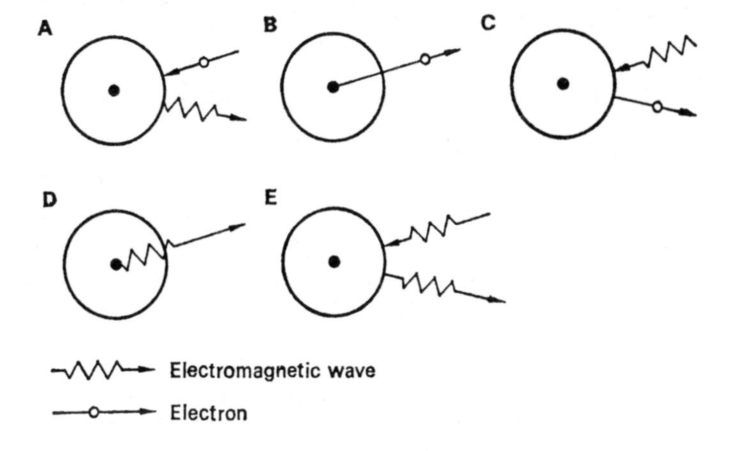

H44 In question **H43**, which diagram illustrates gamma ray emission?

H45 In question **H43**, which diagram illustrates photoelectric emission?

H46 In question **H43**, which diagram illustrates fluorescence?

H47 In question **H43**, which diagram illustrates X-ray emission?

J MECHANICAL WAVES AND SOUND

General wave properties

J1 The ear, unlike the eye, does not produce a focal plane image of the source of the waves (in this case sound waves)
BECAUSE
longitudinal waves cannot be focused.

J2 From the behaviour of the plane waves incident at the lens-shaped area it is possible to deduce that $c_2 > c_1$

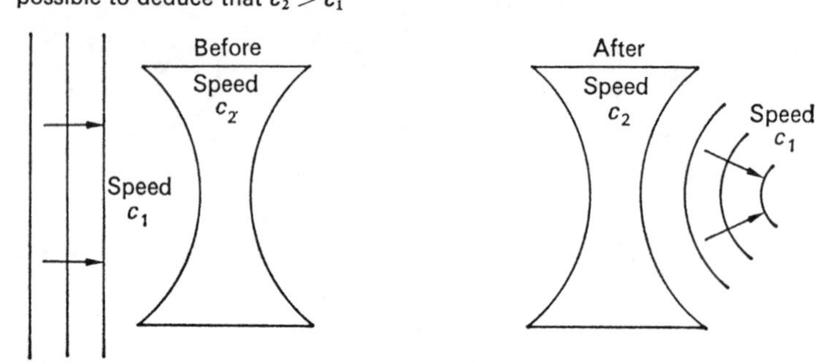

BECAUSE
the middle part of each wavefront travelled a shorter distance than the two edges.

J3 A train of plane waves travelling in deep water is incident on the boundary with some shallow water at an angle θ. In the shallow water they might appear thus

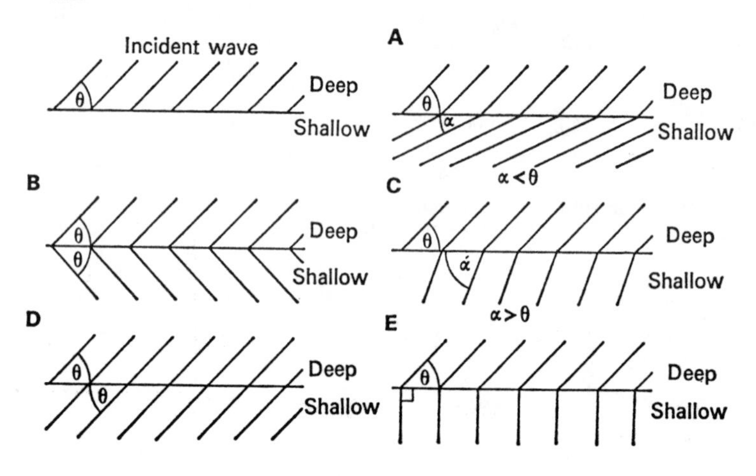

J4 The speed c of an elastic tranverse wave on a stretched membrane (e.g. a drumskin) is thought to depend upon

σ the mass per unit area of the membrane,
λ the wavelength of the wave, and
T the tension in the membrane expressed as the force per unit length of a line in the surface (measured parallel to the surface and perpendicular to the line).
Which expression for c in terms of σ, T and λ is dimensionally valid?

A $\sqrt{\frac{2\pi\sigma}{T}}$ **B** $\sqrt{\frac{\sigma}{T}}$ **C** $\lambda\sqrt{\frac{T}{\sigma}}$ **D** $2\pi\sqrt{\frac{T}{\sigma}}$ **E** $\sqrt{\frac{T}{\sigma\lambda}}$

J5 The speed c of a sound wave travelling through a gas of density ρ, is thought to depend upon the pressupre p of the gas and its absolute temperature T. Which of the following is dimensionally valid?

A $c = \sqrt{\frac{p}{\rho}}$ **B** $c^2 = p\rho T$ **C** $c^2 = \frac{p\rho}{T}$ **D** $c = \frac{T\rho}{p}$ **E** $c = p\rho T$

J6 A disc is painted with one semicircle white and the other black, and is spun clockwise at a steady rotational frequency n_1. In stroboscopic illumination of

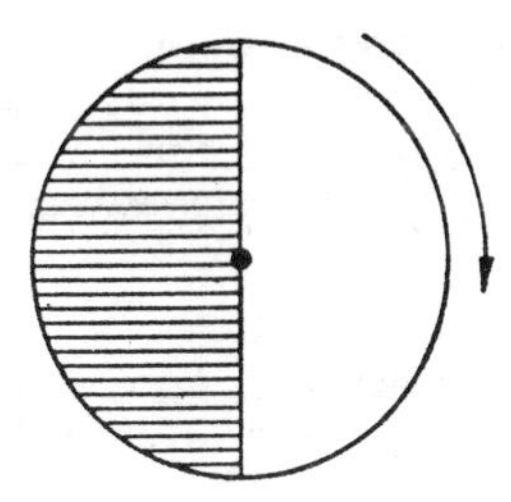

frequency ν ($\approx n_1$) the disc appears to turn slowly clockwise with rotational frequency n_2. Hence n_1 equals

A νn_2 **B** $\nu + n_2$ **C** $\nu - n_2$ **D** $\nu + \frac{\nu}{n_2}$ **E** $\nu - \frac{\nu}{n_2}$

J7 A stroboscope is used to illuminate a plain square panel which spins in its own plane about an axis through its centre, with rotational frequency 60 s^{-1}. Which of the following settings for the stroboscope will produce a square image?

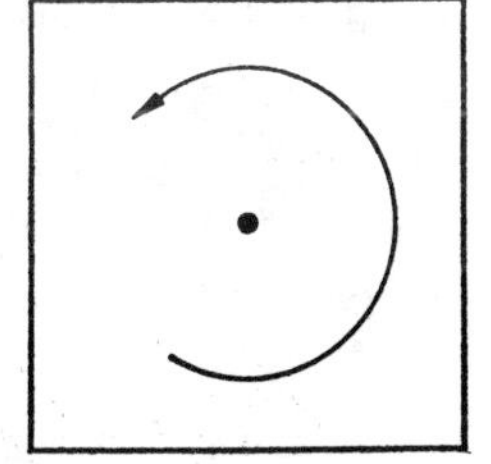

1 20 s^{-1} **2** 30 s^{-1} **3** 120 s^{-1}
4 180 s^{-1}

Progressive waves

J8 A wave pulse is moving, as illustrated, with uniform speed c along a rope.

A graph of displacement s against time t for the point P would be

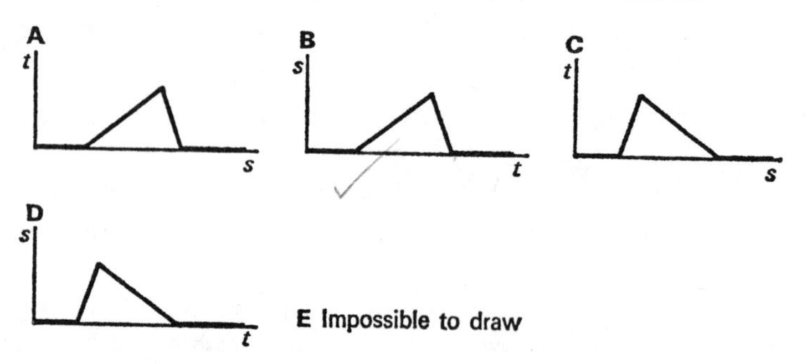

E Impossible to draw

J9 A wave pulse is sent along a spring (shown diagrammatically in the figure) by moving P rapidly to the right and *keeping it there*. The wave pulse is at QR, and RT is as yet undisturbed. Taking displacements to the right as positive, a graph of displacement s against position x would look like

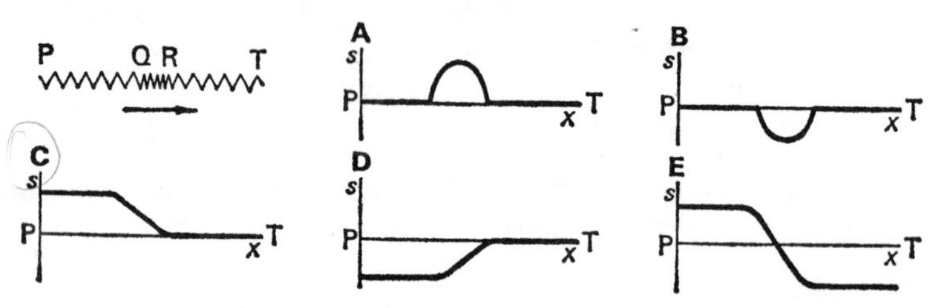

J10 A wave pulse is travelling along a taut spring anchored to a heavy wall. After reflection from the wall the string might show the wave pulse as

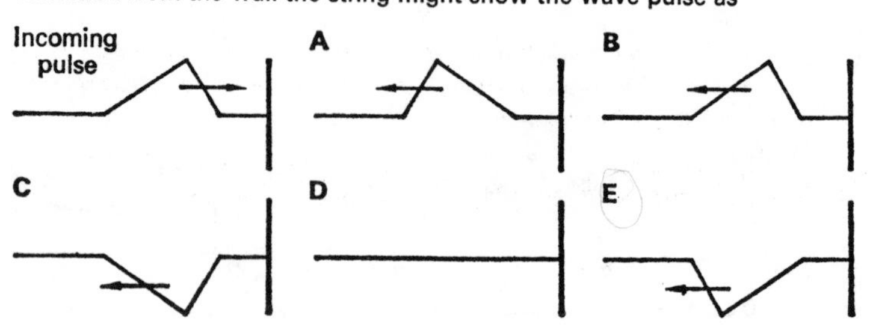

J11 A wave pulse is travelling along a light taut string which ends in a frictionless ring which is free to move in a transverse direction. After reflection, the string might show the wave pulse as

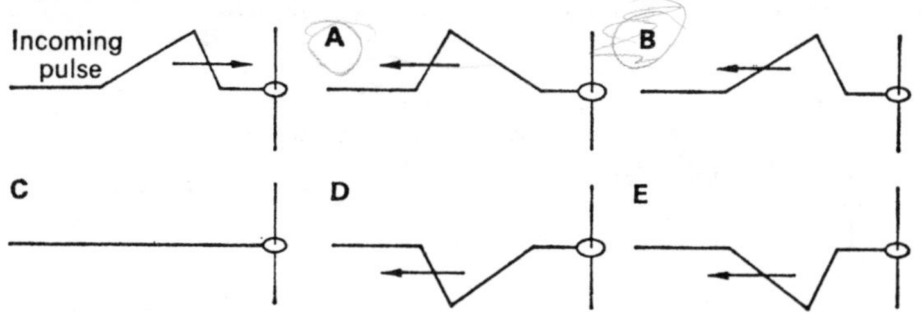

J12 If the rope shown at an instant in the figure is carrying a progressive (travelling)

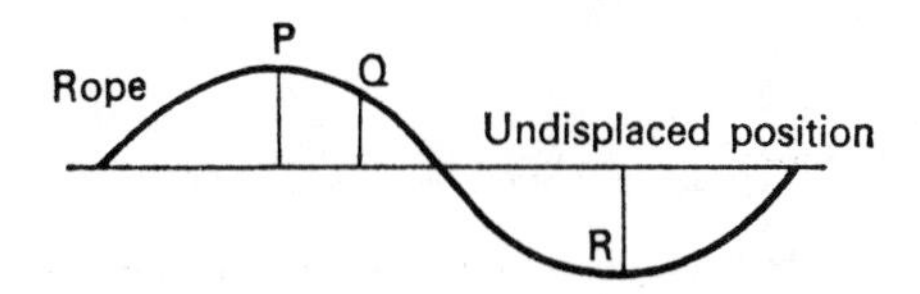

wave from left to right, the phase difference between points P and R is

A zero **B** $\frac{\pi}{2}$ **C** π **D** $\frac{3\pi}{2}$ **E** 2π

The principle of superposition

J13 The principle of superposition, which states that the displacement at a point in the path of two waves is equal to the vector sum of the displacements of the two waves, is true for

1 transverse waves
2 mechanical waves
3 electromagnetic waves
4 longitudinal waves

J14 The first diagram represents the displacement-time graphs for notes of 400 Hz and 1200 Hz respectively. The resultant displacement, at a point subject to both of these, would vary as shown in

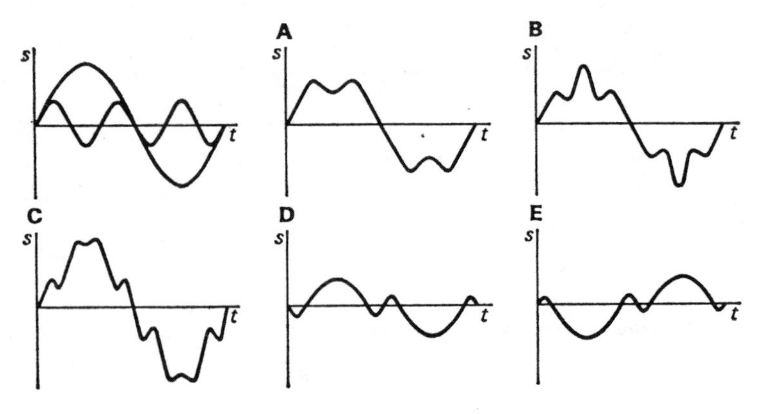

J15 The phase difference ϕ, at P, between waves each of wavelength λ, from

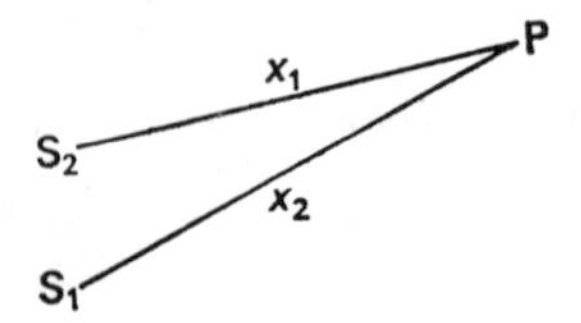

sources at S_1 and S_2 is given by $\phi = \frac{2\pi}{\lambda}(x_1 - x_2) + \epsilon$, where ϵ is

A the distance S_1S_2 **B** the angle S_1PS_2 **C** $\pi/2$
D the phase difference between the sources
E the optical path difference between the waves

J16 Two loudspeakers S_1 and S_2, driven from the same audio oscillator and so maintained in phase, are each emitting sound of wavelength 0.80 m. A

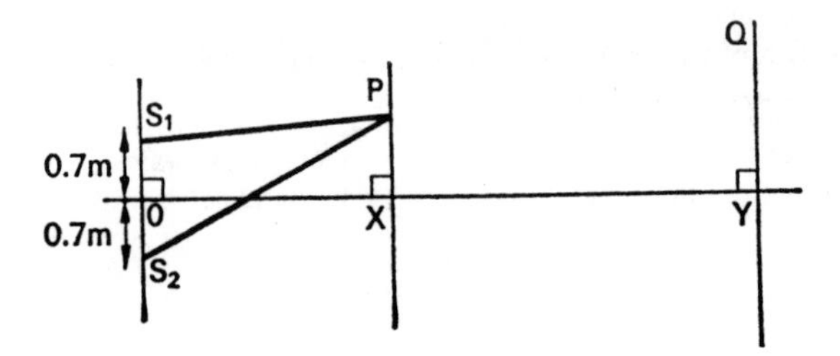

microphone is moved from X perpendicular to OX and records its first minimum signal at P. If $S_1P = 4.0$ m then S_2P is equal to

A 4.4 m **B** 4.7 m **C** $4.0 + \left(\frac{0.4}{1.4}\right) 4.0$ m **D** 4.8 m

E a calculable fraction of *OX*

J17 Referring again to the figure of question **J16**, the microphone is now moved from Y, perpendicular to OY, where $OX = XY$, and records its first minimum signal at Q. Then

1 $QY = 2PX$ **2** $QY > PX$ **3** O, P and Q lie on a straight line
4 $QY > 2PX$

J18 If two coherent sources of sound of frequency f lie some distance away to the north-west and to the north-east, an observer will find a sound wave of frequency $f\sqrt{2}$ travelling due south
BECAUSE
the two frequencies combine as vectors according to the parallelogram law.

J19 In a ripple tank, prods P and Q vibrate in phase. The waves from P and Q

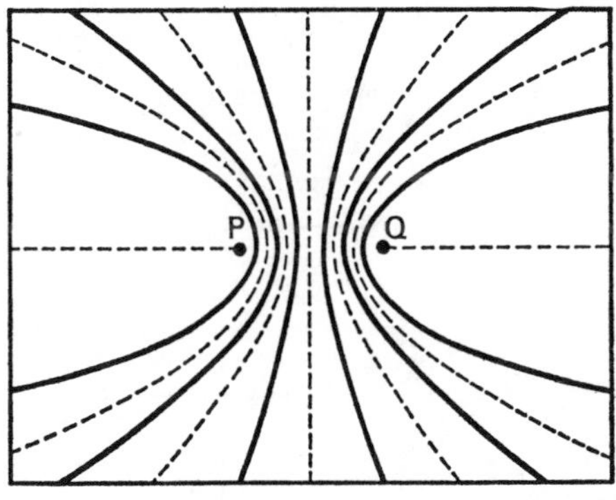

superpose constructively along the firm lines and destructively along the broken lines. The wavelength of the ripples is (see diagram) approximately

A $\frac{PQ}{48}$ **B** $\frac{PQ}{24}$ **C** $\frac{PQ}{12}$ **D** $\frac{PQ}{6}$ **E** $\frac{PQ}{3}$

Stationary waves

J20 If the rope shown at an instant in the figure of question **J12** is vibrating in a stationary mode, the phase difference between points P and Q is

A zero **B** $\frac{\pi}{4}$ **C** $\frac{\pi}{2}$ **D** $\frac{3\pi}{4}$ **E** π

J21 In order to make the playing of a guitar easier the strings are all stretched to roughly the same tension. To cover a wide range of frequencies

1 the strings must be of different lengths
2 some strings are pushed down further than others so as to tighten them when playing a particular note
3 necessarily involves using a separate amplifying circuit for each string
4 the strings are made of materials of different mass per unit length

J22 The air in a tube which is open at both ends is resonating at 1320 Hz in its fundamental mode. If the speed of sound in air is 330 m s^{-1} then the length of the tube is about

A $\frac{1}{4}\left(\frac{330}{1320}\right)$ m **B** $\frac{1}{2}\left(\frac{330}{1320}\right)$ m **C** $\frac{330}{1320}$ m **D** $\frac{3}{2}\left(\frac{330}{1320}\right)$ m **E** $2\left(\frac{330}{1320}\right)$ m

J23 Two straight, stiff bars, each of length L, are fastened together at right angles and used in a water tank to generate regular plane ripples of wavelength $L/2$.

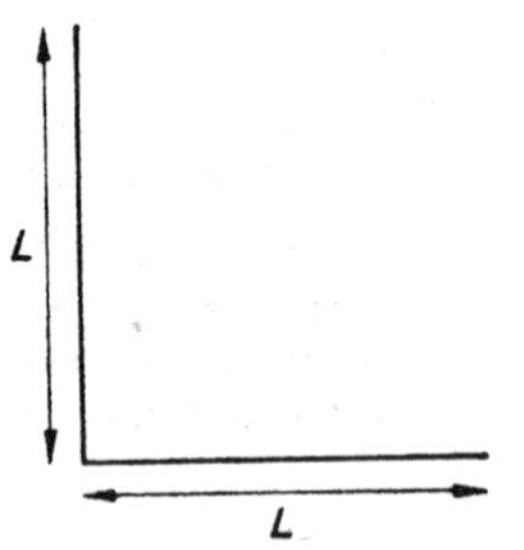

A No stationary interference pattern is produced since the waves travel at 90° to each other

alternatively

the water oscillates only in the areas shown cross-hatched in

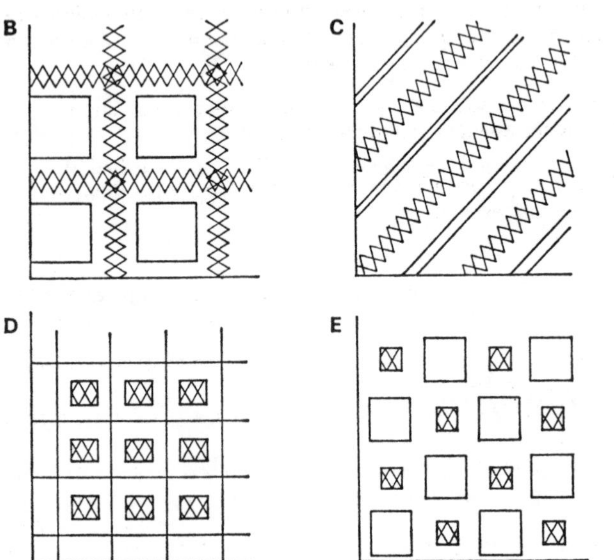

Properties of sound waves

J24 A bat emits an ultrasonic sound wave at 33.0 kHz and receives an echo 100 ms later. If the speed of sound in air is 330 m s^{-1} the distance of the bat from the object producing the echo is

A 10.0 m **B** 16.5 m **C** 20.0 m **D** 33.0 m **E** 66.0 m

J25 The sound carried by air from a violin to a listener is a

A longitudinal stationary mechanical wave motion
B transverse progressive electromagnetic wave motion
C transverse stationary mechanical wave motion
D longitudinal progressive mechanical wave motion
E longitudinal progressive electromagnetic wave motion

J26 The speed at which sound waves of audible frequencies and intensities travel through a fluid depends upon

1 the density of the fluid
2 the frequency of the sound
3 the bulk (or compressional) modulus of elasticity of the fluid
4 the loudness of the sound

J27 In order to calculate the speed of propagation of an audible sound wave in nitrogen gas at 300 K, you are told that nitrogen is a diatomic gas for which $\gamma = 1.4$. You will also need to know

A the density at 300 K and the mass of one mole of nitrogen
B only the pressure of nitrogen at 300 K
C the pressure of nitrogen at 300 K and the gas constant, R
D the mass of one mole of nitrogen and the gas constant, R
E only the gas constant, R

J28 A man at P hears a man at Q cough quite distinctly when P is 200 m from Q across a flat field. Possible contributory factors to this effect are that

1 the air could be very still with a vertical temperature gradient—the coldest air close to the ground
2 there could be a wind blowing from P to Q with its lowest speed close to the ground
3 there could be a wind blowing from Q to P with its lowest speed close to the ground
4 the air could be very still with a vertical temperature gradient—the hottest air close to the ground

J29 The speed of deep water waves varies with frequency approximately as shown.

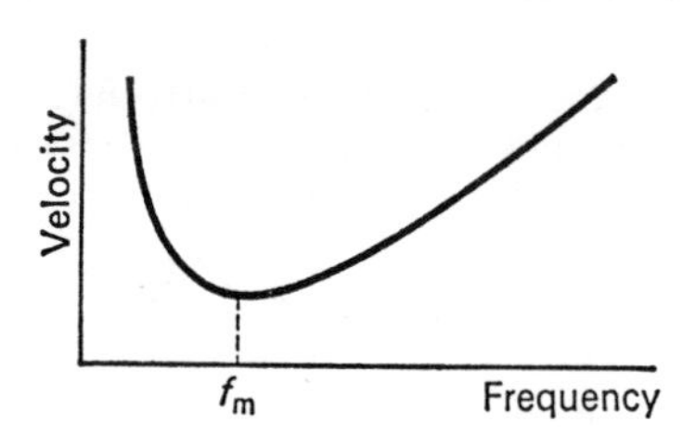

If the speed of sound waves varied in a similar way, a sudden distant noise (spanning this range of frequencies) would

A be heard first at frequency f_m
B be loudest at frequency f_m
C be heard at ground level at frequency f_m only
D be heard as exactly the same sound as under present, normal conditions
E be heard as a musical sequence finishing at frequency f_m

J30 Plane sound waves are refracted as shown at a thin flat membrane separating warm air and cold air.

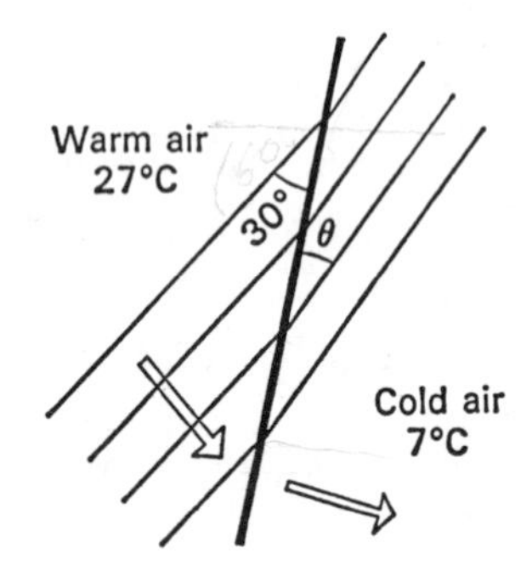

A $\sin^2\theta = 27/28$ **B** $\sin^2\theta = 14/15$ **C** $\sin^2\theta = 1/2$ **D** $\sin^2\theta = 7/15$

E $\sin^2\theta = 7/30$

Sound phenomena

J31 An observer is standing some distance in front of a long straight stone staircase. He claps his hands together just once and hears a ringing tone of frequency 660 Hz. If the speed of sound in air is 330 m s^{-1} the horizontal depth of each step is

A 0.25 m **B** 0.50 m **C** 0.75 m **D** 1.0 m
E impossible to estimate from these figures

J32 As a girl stops singing a note she is surprised to hear an echo of higher frequency i.e. of higher musical pitch.

1 There could be some warm air between the girl and a fixed reflecting surface
2 There could be two identical fixed reflecting surfaces, one a quarter of a wavelength further away than the other
3 The girl could be moving away from a fixed reflecting surface
4 There could be a reflecting surface which is moving towards the girl

J33 Superposition of two sound wavetrains could give rise to beats or to a stationary wave pattern. Essential to the observation of *both of these* are the following features of the two wavetrains:

1 the lines of travel must be identical
2 the amplitudes must be roughly equal
3 the frequencies must be identical
4 the sources of the sound must be perfectly stationary

J34 An oscilloscope is fed by a microphone which receives simultaneously a 50 Hz signal and one of higher frequency f. The first diagram shows the trace with

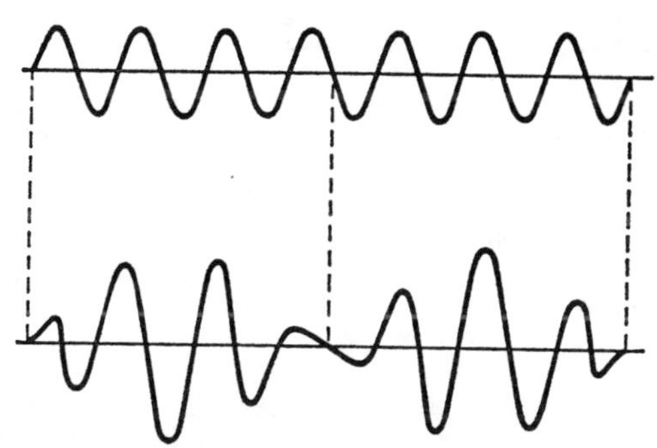

the 50 Hz signal alone while the second shows the trace due to the combined signals. This indicates a beat frequency of

A $\frac{1}{7} \times 50$ Hz **B** $\frac{2}{7} \times 50$ Hz **C** $\frac{5}{2} \times 50$ Hz **D** $\frac{7}{2} \times 50$ Hz **E** 7×50 Hz

J35 Using your conclusion in the previous question, it follows that f must be

A $\frac{3}{2} \times 50$ Hz **B** $\frac{4}{3} \times 50$ Hz **C** $\frac{5}{4} \times 50$ Hz **D** $\frac{7}{5} \times 50$ Hz **E** $\frac{9}{7} \times 50$ Hz

J36 An organ pipe emits sound, and a gas discharge tube emits light, both in a series of discrete frequencies and with well defined amplitudes, s_0. Sketches (i) and (ii) indicate strict limits imposed on the series, while (iii) shows no limit. Ignore variations of amplitude.

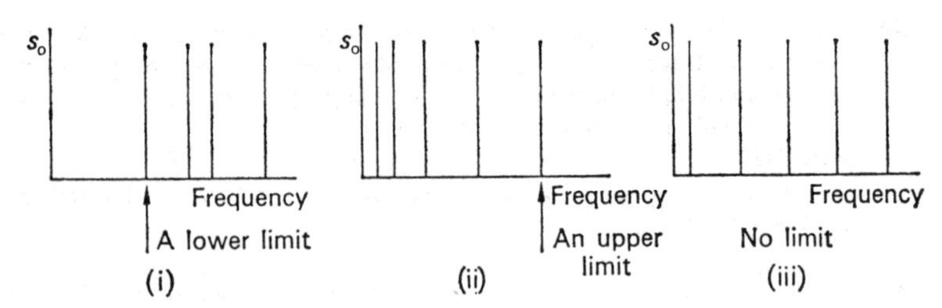

A (i) is for the pipe and the tube
B (ii) is for the pipe; (i) for the tube
C (iii) is for the pipe; (i) for the tube
D (ii) is for the pipe and the tube
E (i) is for the pipe; (ii) for the tube

K PHYSICAL OPTICS

Interference: division of wavefront

K1 The phase difference between two wavetrains giving rise to a dark fringe in a Young's slits experiment,—taking n as an integer—is

A zero **B** $2\pi n + \frac{\pi}{8}$ **C** $2\pi n + \frac{\pi}{4}$ **D** $2\pi n + \frac{\pi}{2}$ **E** $2\pi n + \pi$

K2 In an experiment to demonstrate interference of light using Young's slits, the separation of the two narrow slits is doubled. In order to maintain the same spacing of the fringes, the distance, D, of the screen from the slits must now be altered to about

A $\frac{1}{2}D$ **B** $\frac{D}{\sqrt{2}}$ **C** $\sqrt{2}D$ **D** $2D$ **E** $4D$

K3 If one of the twin slits of a standard Young's slits demonstration of interference in light is painted over so that it transmits only half the light intensity of the other,

A the fringe system will vanish completely
B the bright lines will be brighter and the dark lines darker
C the bright lines and the dark lines will all be darker
D the bright lines and the dark lines will all be brighter
E the dark lines will be brighter and the bright lines darker

K4 A person views the interference pattern produced using two slits illuminated by white light and, on placing a green filter in front of his eye, sees a pattern of dark and bright green fringes. On exchanging the green filter for a violet filter, the bright lines are seen closer together
BECAUSE
the violet filter transmits light of a longer wavelength than that transmitted by the green filter.

K5 In a standard Young's slits experiment, the twin slits are separated by a small gap s, and placed at a distance D from the screen on which the fringes are formed. With light of wavelength λ the number of fringes per metre on the screen will be

A $\frac{Ds}{\lambda}$ **B** $\frac{D\lambda}{s}$ **C** $\frac{\lambda s}{D}$ **D** $\frac{D}{s}$ **E** $\frac{s}{D\lambda}$

K6 In a Young's slits experiment

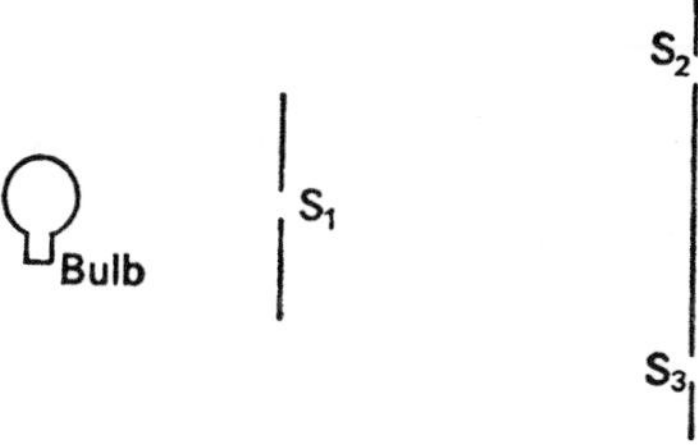

1 S_1 is used to produce coherent light sources at S_2 and S_3
2 S_1 is used to reduce the amount of light incident upon S_2 and S_3
3 the width of the slits S_2 and S_3 must be as small as is physically possible
4 S_2 and S_3 must be an integral number of wavelengths apart

K7 Interference fringes were produced with white light by a double slit arrangement. When a piece of parallel-sided mica of refractive index 1.6 relative to air was placed in front of *one* of the slits, the centre of the fringe system moved to the left a distance subsequently shown to accommodate 30 dark bands when using light of wavelength 480 nm. To two significant figures the thickness of the mica is

A 0.090 mm **B** 0.012 mm **C** 0.014 mm **D** 0.024 mm **E** 0.062 mm

K8 In an experiment to demonstrate interference of light using Young's slits, the

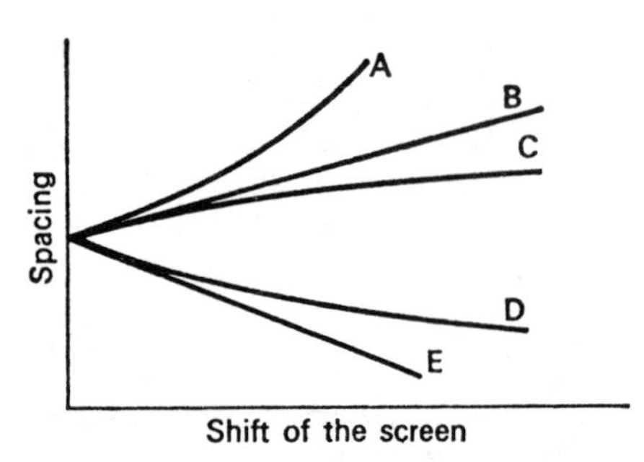

screen is moved steadily away from the slits. The spacing of the fringes on the screen will theoretically,

A increase at an accelerating rate
B increase at a uniform rate
C increase at a slower and slower rate
D decrease at a falling rate
E decrease at a uniform rate

Interference : division of amplitude

K9 In an experiment with Newton's rings it is found that, towards the edge of the pattern, the dark rings

A get closer together and thinner
B get closer together but remain of equal thickness
C are equally spaced but get thinner
D get further apart but remain of equal thickness
E get further apart and thinner

K10 When a photographic transparency of Newton's rings is laid on graph paper, it is observed that the centre dark spot and the first two dark rings just fit the middle square. What is the number of the ring which, as shown, just fits into nine squares? (See figure at head of opposite page.)

A 6 **B** 9 **C** 12 **D** 18 **E** 27

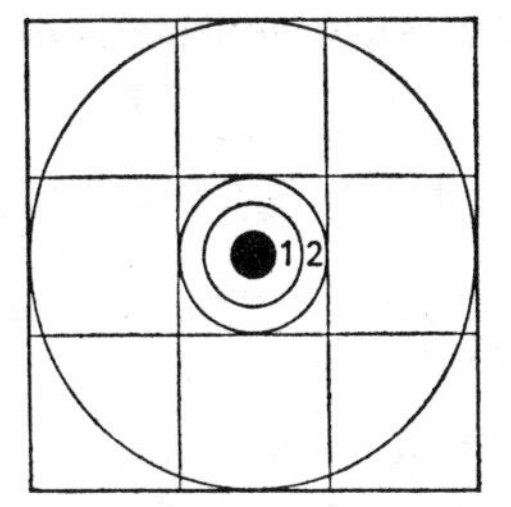

K11 In an experiment with Newton's rings, the lens is slowly lifted until it is one

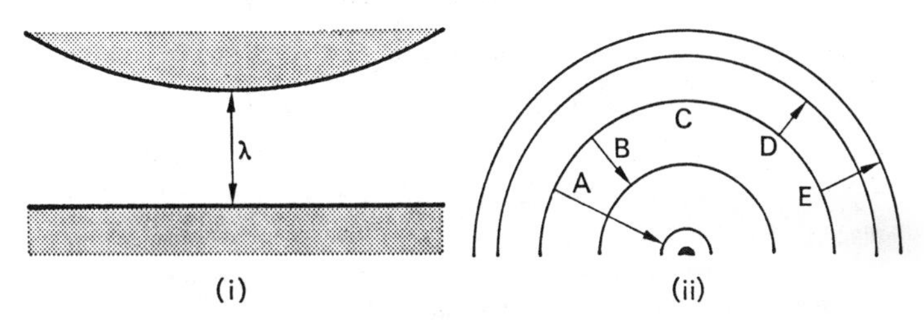

wavelength (λ) clear of the plate, see figure (i). The dark rings—see figure (ii) —will

A move in towards the centre two places
B move in towards the centre one place
C remain stationary
D move out from the centre one place
E move out from the centre two places

K12 A liquid of refractive index 4/3 is allowed to displace the air from an air wedge

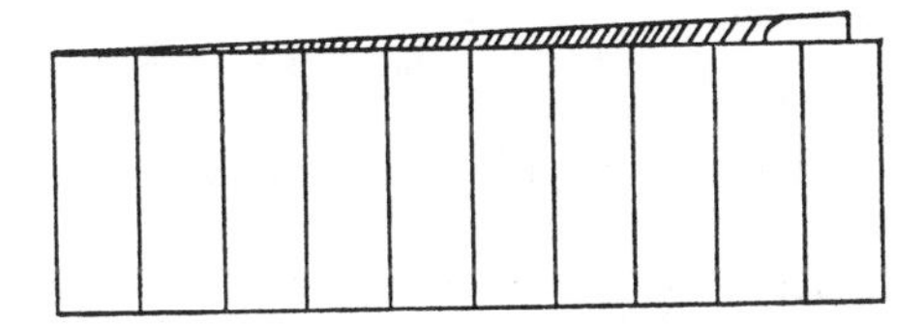

formed from two glass plates touching each other along one edge. The spacing of the dark lines caused by interference in the reflected light

A increases to 4/3 times its original value
B increases to three times its original value
C remains the same
D decreases to 3/4 of its first value
E decreases to one third of its first value

K13 In an air wedge formed by two plane glass plates touching each other at the left hand edge, there are 4001 dark lines observable when it is viewed by reflected, highly monochromatic light.

When the air between the plates is evacuated, this falls to 4000. The refractive index of the air is therefore

A 0.00025 **B** 0.00050 **C** 1.00025 **D** 1.00050 **E** 0.99975

K14 A transmitter, T, of electromagnetic waves of wavelength λ is set facing two plane hardboard reflectors X and Y. The first reflector, X, transmits

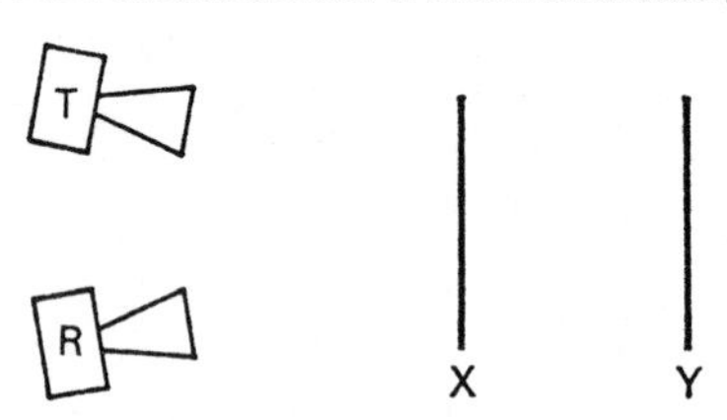

75 per cent and reflects 25 per cent of the radiation falling on it. A receiver, R, placed so as to receive reflected waves is found to register a small signal. When Y is removed a larger signal is received. If n is an integer then the necessary and sufficient condition for this effect is

A $XY = \frac{n\lambda}{4}$ **B** $XY = \frac{n\lambda}{2}$

C $XY = \frac{n\lambda}{2} + \frac{\lambda}{4}$ **D** $XY = n\lambda + \frac{\lambda}{4}$

E $XY = n\lambda + \frac{\lambda}{2}$

K15 A soap film is formed on a wire ring, held vertically and allowed to drain. A diffuse source of white light is observed by reflection in the soap film.

1 Just before the film breaks it may appear black at the top
2 The bands of colour move downwards as the film drains
3 The thickness of the film is of the same order as the wavelength of visible light
4 The colours are due to refraction of light by the wedge-shaped film

K16 In an air wedge formed from two plane glass plates touching each other at the left hand edge there are ten dark bands due to interference when it is viewed by reflected monochromatic light. If the left hand edge of the top plate is now lifted slowly away from the other until the two plates are parallel,

A the dark bands crowd together towards the right hand edge of the plates
B the dark bands remain stationary
C the dark bands crowd together towards the left hand edge of the plates
D the dark bands spread out, disappearing off the right hand edge of the plates
E the dark bands spread out, disappearing off the left hand edge of the plates

Diffraction

K17 One can sharpen the image in a pinhole camera by reducing the diameter d of the pinhole. There is, however, a minimum useful diameter
BECAUSE
as d decreases, blurring due to diffraction increases.

K18 Monochromatic light from a distant point source falls on a diffraction grating set with its lines vertical and its plane at right angles to the incident light. An observer whose eye is close to the grating sees, with his eye relaxed,

A the point source only
B a horizontal haze of light
C the point source with continuous spectra on both sides
D the point source with subsidiary images of the source on both sides
E a sequence of fine vertical lines

K19 With light of normal incidence, of wavelength λ, a diffraction grating G gives

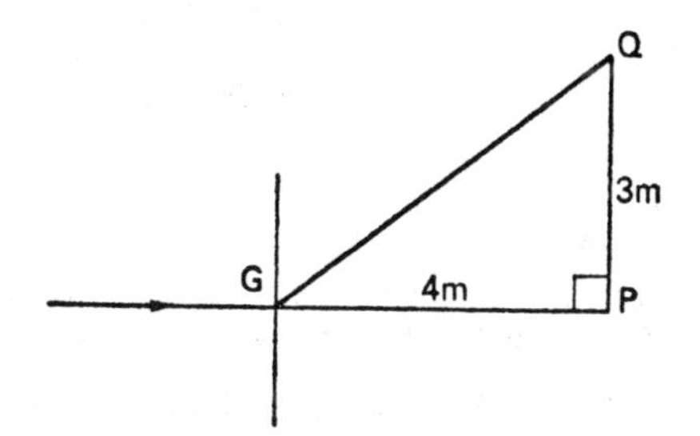

a central maximum along GP, and a first diffracted maximum in the direction GQ. The spacing of the lines on the grating is

A $\frac{3}{5}\lambda$ **B** $\frac{3}{4}\lambda$ **C** $\frac{4}{5}\lambda$ **D** $\frac{5}{4}\lambda$ **E** $\frac{5}{3}\lambda$

K20 The spacing of the lines of a diffraction grating is 3λ where λ is the wavelength of the monochromatic light falling on it at normal incidence. The deviation θ of the first diffracted beam is given by

A $\sin \theta/2 = 1/3$ **B** $\sin \theta/3 = 2/3$ **C** $\sin \theta = 1/3$ **D** $\tan \theta/2 = 1/3$
E $\tan \theta = 2/3$

K21 Monochromatic light falls with normal incidence on a diffraction grating replica

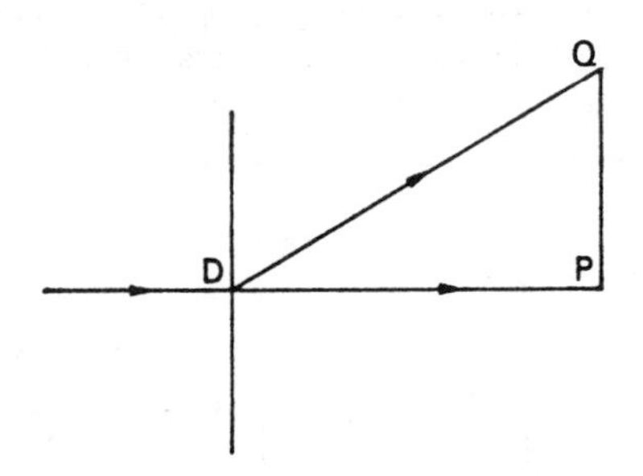

D. If the replica shrinks by one per cent in all of its dimensions, the displacement PQ of the first maximum on a distant screen

A increases by 1% **B** increases by $\frac{1}{2}$% **C** remains unaltered
D decreases by $\frac{1}{2}$% **E** decreases by 1%

K22 A diffraction grating of width S, produces a deviation θ in the second order with light of wavelength λ. The total number N of lines on the grating is given by

A $\sin\theta = \frac{2S\lambda}{N}$ **B** $\sin\theta = \frac{N\lambda}{S}$ **C** $\sin\theta = \frac{\lambda S}{2N}$ **D** $\sin\theta = \frac{2\lambda N}{S}$ **E** $\sin\theta = \frac{2\lambda}{N}$

K23 Let s be the distance between adjacent gaps in an optical diffraction grating,

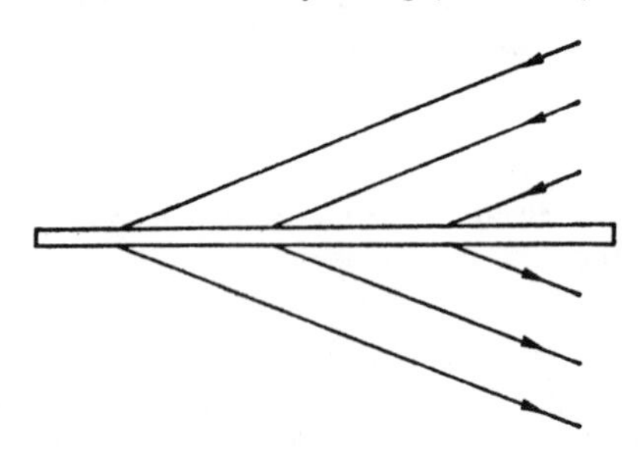

and λ the wavelength of the light incident upon the grating. If a first order spectrum can be seen only by arranging the grating as shown, then

A $\frac{2s}{\lambda}$ cannot be estimated **B** $\frac{2s}{\lambda} \geqslant 1$ **C** $\frac{2s}{\lambda} \gg 1$

D $\frac{2s}{\lambda} \leqslant 1$ **E** $\frac{2s}{\lambda} \ll 1$

K24 A narrow shaft of white light (from violet, 400 nm, to red 700 nm) falls with normal incidence on a transmission grating, and produces two orders of spectra on a distant screen. The appearance of these will be as in the diagram

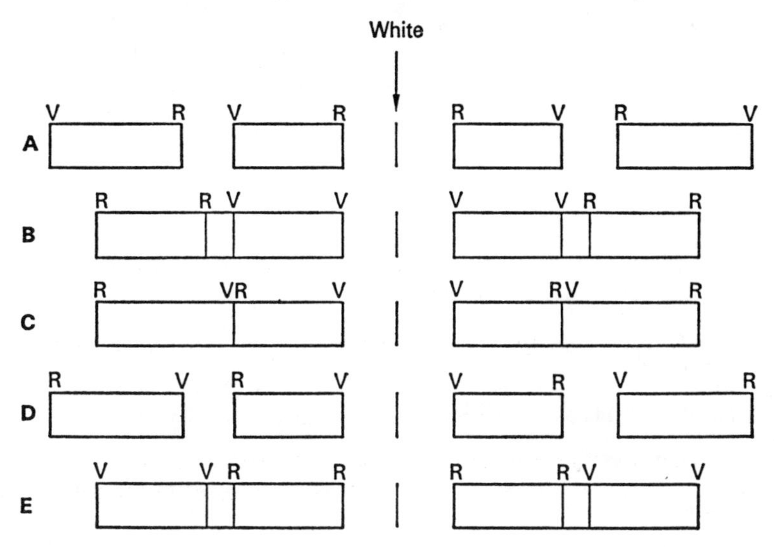

K25 A diffraction grating is to be able just to resolve in the first order spectrum wavelengths of 400.0 and 400.1 nm. The number of lines in the grating must be

A 400 **B** 800 **C** 1000 **D** 2000 **E** 4000

Polarisation

K26 A clear sheet of polaroid is placed on top of a similar sheet so that their polarising axes make an angle of 30° to each other. The ratio of the intensity of emergent light to that of the unpolarised incident light is

A 1:4 **B** 1:3 **C** 1:2 **D** 3:4 **E** 3:8

K27 Light, travelling in water ($n_W = 1.33$), is incident upon a plate of glass ($n_g = 1.53$). To the nearest degree at what angle of incidence is the reflected light plane polarised?

A 41° **B** 43° **C** 45° **D** 47° **E** 49°

K28 A transistor radio equipped with only a horizontal ferrite bar aerial, fades out if turned on end so that the bar is vertical. The magnetic wave (the magnetic component of the electromagnetic radio wave) is therefore

A longitudinal, and horizontally polarised
B longitudinal, and vertically polarised
C transverse, and horizontally polarised
D transverse, and vertically polarised
E transverse, and longitudinally polarised

The electromagnetic spectrum

K29 When light passes from air into glass it experiences a change of

A frequency, speed and wavelength
B frequency and speed
C speed and wavelength
D frequency and wavelength
E speed only

K30 The Fraunhofer lines are evidence of

A the complete absence of certain elements in the Sun
B the absence of certain elements in the Sun's interior
C the absence of certain elements in the Sun's surface layers
D the presence of certain elements in the Sun's surface layers
E the presence of certain elements in the Sun's interior

K31 The following is a list of sources of electromagnetic waves:

p — mains transformer
q — BBC Radio One transmitter
r — 30 mm radar transmitter
s — yellow (sodium) street lamp

Which of the following correctly places them in order of decreasing wavelength?

A p q r s **B** q p r s **C** q p s r **D** p r q s **E** s r p q

K32 The energy delivered per second by any beam of blue light *must* be greater than the energy delivered by a beam of red light
BECAUSE
a photon of blue light has more energy than a photon of red light.

K33 In the equation $c\epsilon_0\mu_0 = k$, where ϵ_0 and μ_0 are the permittivity and permeability of a vacuum respectively and c is the speed of propagation of electromagnetic waves in a vacuum, k has

A the unit m s^{-1}
B the unit m^{-1} s
C the unit F s^{-1} (F = farad)
D the unit H s^{-1} (H = henry)
E no units, i.e. it is a dimensionless quantity

K34 X-rays

1 produce ionisation of the air through which they pass
2 affect photographic emulsions
3 have a penetrating power proportional to the anode–cathode potential difference in the tube producing the X-rays
4 cannot be diffracted as their wavelength is too small

K35 X-rays originate at places on a metal where high speed electrons are suddenly stopped. The kinetic energy of the electrons

A all becomes internal energy of the target material
B mostly becomes electromagnetic wave energy of the X-rays
C all becomes kinetic energy of the X-rays
D mostly becomes internal energy of the target material
E mostly becomes kinetic energy of the conduction electrons of the target material

K36 The intensity of X-rays a certain distance from their source depends on

1 the square of the distance from the source
2 the atomic number of the target material used in the source
3 the current through the X-ray tube forming the source
4 the potential difference between the electrodes in the X-ray tube forming the source

L GEOMETRIC OPTICS

Refraction

L1 A ray of light is travelling in water (refractive index n_1) and is incident on the air boundary at the critical angle. When a layer of oil (refractive index n_2) is floated upon the water surface, the angle, measured in the oil, between the ray and the perpendicular to the surface of the oil is given by

A $\sin^{-1} 1.00$ **B** $\sin^{-1}\frac{1}{n_1}$ **C** $\sin^{-1}\frac{1}{n_2}$ **D** $\sin^{-1}\frac{n_1}{n_2}$ **E** $\sin^{-1}\frac{n_2}{n_1}$

L2 A fish is swimming in a large pond which has clear water and a calm surface. On looking toward the surface he might see

1 all the sky
2 a mirrorlike reflection of himself
3 a mirrorlike reflection of part of the bottom of the pond
4 an amount of the sky which is dependent upon the depth of water above the fish

L3 If blue light has a velocity of 3.00×10^8 m s^{-1} in air, its velocity in water ($n = 1.33$) is k $\times 10^8$ m s^{-1}, where k is

A 1.00 **B** 2.25 **C** 2.33 **D** 4.00 **E** 9.00

L4 When the Sun is close to the horizon a diameter drawn vertically across its disc will subtend a larger angle than that subtended by a diameter drawn horizontally
BECAUSE
the speed of light in air is greater than the speed of light in a vacuum.

L5 The refractive indices of water and glass are 4/3 and 3/2 respectively. The refractive index of water relative to glass is

A $\frac{1}{2}$ **B** $\frac{8}{9}$ **C** $\frac{9}{8}$ **D** minus $\frac{1}{6}$ **E** 2

L6 When a thin prism of refracting angle A and refractive index n_1 is immersed in a medium of refractive index n_2, a ray of light incident at a small angle to the normal will be deviated through an angle d, where $\frac{d}{A}$ is

A $\frac{n_2}{n_1} - 1$ **B** $\frac{n_1}{n_2} - 1$ **C** $1 - \frac{n_2}{n_1}$ **D** $1 - \frac{n_1}{n_2}$ **E** $n_1 - n_2$

L7 A ray of light is incident upon a prism of refracting angle A and emerges as shown in the diagram. (Do not consider cases involving total internal reflection at the second face.)

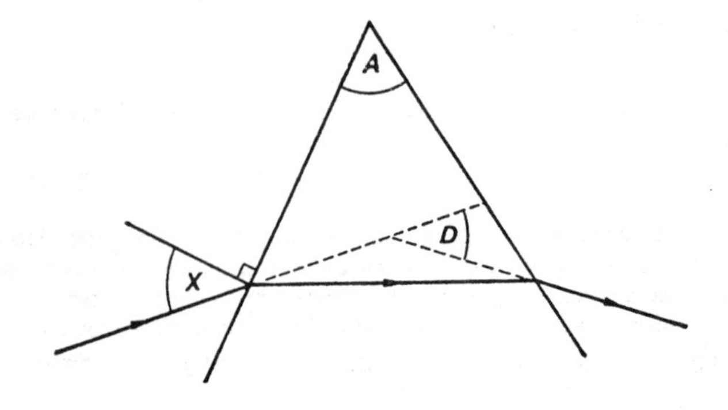

1 As the angle X increases from zero the angle of deviation passes through a maximum value
2 At any particular value of X, the angle D depends both upon the refracting angle, A, and the refractive index of the prism relative to the surrounding medium
3 The deviation, D, is zero when the ray enters the prism normally
4 If the refracting angle, A, is increased, so is the deviation D

L8 Measurements on a prism show that it has a refracting angle of 60.0°, and an angle of minimum deviation for yellow light of 40.0°. The measured refractive index relative to air for the glass using yellow light is

A 1.50 **B** 1.53 **C** 1.56 **D** 1.67 **E** 1.74

L9 The shadow of a vertical flag-pole cast by the sun has clearly-defined edges near its base, but less-well-defined edges near its top end. This is principally caused by

A the humidity of the atmosphere
B the variation of the refractive index of air with altitude
C the finite angle subtended by the Sun
D Brownian motion
E diffraction

L10 A lens forms a sharp image on a screen. On inserting a parallel-sided slab of perspex between the lens and the screen it is found necessary to move the screen a distance d away from the lens in order for the image to be again sharply focused. If the refractive index of perspex relative to air is n, then the thickness of the slab of perspex is

A $\frac{d}{n}$ **B** d **C** nd **D** $\frac{nd}{n-1}$ **E** $\frac{(n-1)d}{n}$

Spherical mirrors

L11 The focal length of a spherical mirror is N times its radius of curvature, where N is

A 0.25 **B** 0.5 **C** 1.0 **D** 2.0 **E** 4.0

L12 A concave spherical mirror, with radius of curvature 200 mm, is placed with its hollow side upwards and its principal axis vertical. When a little liquid is poured into the mirror, a pin placed 150 mm above it is found to coincide with its own image. The refractive index of the liquid relative to that of air is

A 1.33 **B** 1.38 **C** 1.40 **D** 1.50 **E** 1.66

L13 A small object is placed across the principal axis of a concave spherical mirror between its principal focus and its pole. The image formed by the mirror is

A virtual, inverted and diminished
B real, inverted and diminished
C virtual, erect and magnified
D real, erect and diminished
E real, inverted and magnified

L14 The image of a small object placed across the principal axis of a convex spherical mirror is

1 always virtual
2 always erect
3 always diminished
4 always between the principal focus of the mirror and its centre of curvature

Spherical lenses

L15 The distance between an object and its three-times magnified real image, produced by a converging lens, is 400 mm. If the magnification is to be increased to five, the distance between object and image must change to

A 360 mm **B** 540 mm **C** 600 mm **D** 720 mm **E** 960 mm

L16 A converging lens produces a real image of an object. The figure shows the object as seen from the lens. Which diagram shows the image as seen *from the lens*?

Object

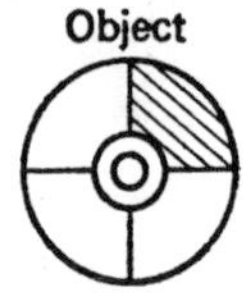

A

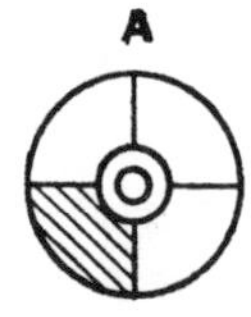

B

C

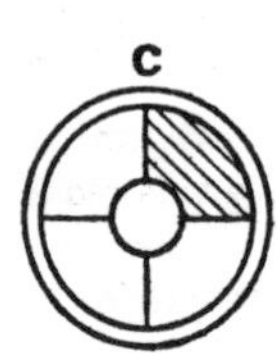

D

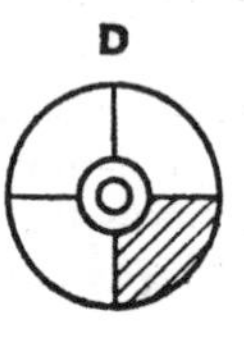

E

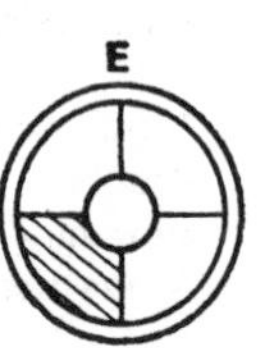

A Upside down and the wrong way round
B The wrong way round
C Inside out
D Upside down
E Upside down, inside out, and the wrong way round

L17 A *virtual* object is arranged to lie between a diverging spherical lens and its principal focus. The image formed by the lens is

A real, erect and magnified
B real, inverted and magnified
C virtual, inverted and magnified
D virtual, erect and diminished
E virtual, inverted and diminished

L18 A graph is plotted of u against $u+v$ for real images formed by a converging spherical lens of focal length f. The value obtained for the minimum of $u+v$ is found to be

A f **B** $2f$ **C** $4f$ **D** f^2 **E** f^2+2f

L19 The ray diagram could be correct

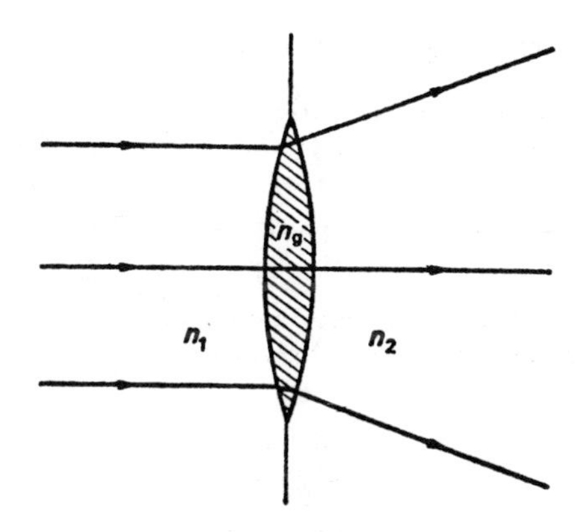

1 if $n_2 > n_1 > n_g$
2 if $n_2 = n_1$, and $n_1 < n_g$
3 if $n_2 = n_1$, and $n_g < n_2$
4 under no circumstances

L20 When using the formula $\frac{1}{f} = \left(\frac{n_2}{n_1} - 1\right)\left(\frac{1}{r_1} + \frac{1}{r_2}\right)$,

1 there is no sign convention for r_1 and r_2
2 either r_1 or r_2 is zero if the lens is plano-convex
3 n_2 must be greater than n_1
4 only thin lenses can be considered

L21 The radii of curvature of the spherical surfaces of a converging lens are each 200 mm. The glass has a refractive index of 1.67. The focal length of the lens when immersed in water of refractive index 1.33 is, to two significant figures,

A 120 mm **B** 200 mm **C** 240 mm **D** 300 mm **E** 400 mm

L22 The equivalent focal length of a pair of thin lenses in contact, with focal lengths f_1 and f_2, is

A $f_1 + f_2$ **B** $\frac{f_1 f_2}{f_1 + f_2}$ **C** $\frac{1}{f_1} + \frac{1}{f_2}$ **D** $f_1 - f_2$ **E** $\frac{f_1(f_1 - f_2)}{f_2}$

Lens aberrations

L23 A simple lens forms an image of a point source on its axis; the image suffers from both chromatic and spherical aberration. Four rays of white light from

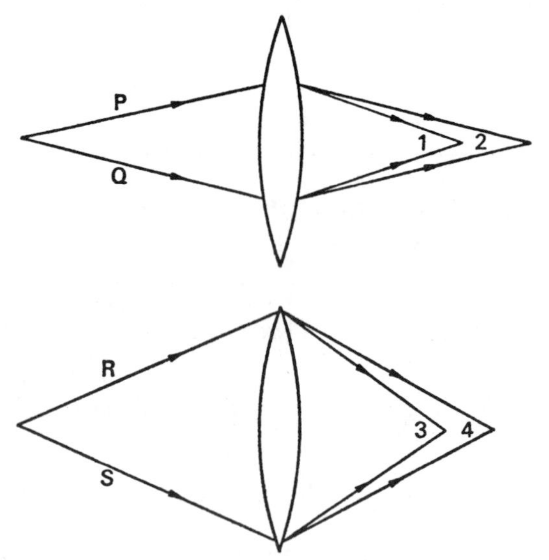

the source are shown (P, Q, R, S) in the diagrams. Chromatic aberration accounts for the gap between the points

A 1 and 2 **B** 1 and 3 **C** 1 and 4 **D** 2 and 4 **E** 2 and 3

L24 In the diagrams above, (question **L23**), spherical aberration accounts for the gap between the points

A 2 and 3 **B** 3 and 4 **C** 4 and 1 **D** 1 and 2 **E** 1 and 3

L25 A simple spherical converging lens forms two distinct images of a point object which is illuminated by light of two colours. (The effect is termed chromatic aberration.) A single image could be formed

A by using a pair of lenses made of the same glass, one converging and one diverging
B by using a pair of lenses made of different glasses, one converging and one diverging
C under no circumstances
D by using a pair of converging lenses made of the same glass
E by using a pair of converging lenses made of different glasses

L26 Spherical aberration in a lens of a certain focal length can be reduced by

1 dividing the deviation required equally between the two faces of the lens
2 reducing the effective aperture of the lens
3 specially shaping the surfaces of the lens
4 ensuring that only monochromatic light passes through the lens

Optical instruments

L27 An observer, whose furthest point of distinct vision is at infinity, uses a magnifying glass right up against his eye. He finds that he can see a clear magnified image of an object if it is held anywhere between 50 mm and 60 mm from the lens, but nowhere else. His least distance of distinct vision

A is 50 mm **B** is 250 mm **C** is 300 mm **D** is 360 mm
E cannot be deduced from these figures

L28 In a simple two-lens refracting microscope, the intermediate image, in normal use, is

A virtual, erect and magnified **B** real, erect and magnified
C real, inverted and magnified **D** virtual, inverted and diminished
E virtual, inverted and magnified

L29 In a simple two-lens refracting microscope, the object is 10 mm from the objective lens. The lenses are 300 mm apart, with the intermediate image 50 mm from the eye lens. If the final image is virtual and 250 mm from the eye lens, then the magnification produced is

A 75 **B** 100 **C** 125 **D** 150 **E** 160

L30 The eyering (or exit pupil) in a simple astronomical telescope consisting of two converging lenses

1 may be smaller than the aperture of the eye lens
2 is the real image of the aperture of the objective lens formed by the eye lens
3 should be about the same diameter as the pupil of the observer's eye
4 lies between the two lenses

L31 The magnifying power of a simple two-lens astronomical telescope in normal adjustment is 36, and the diameter of the objective lens is 72 mm. The minimum diameter of the eyepiece required to collect all the light entering the objective from a distant point source on the axis of the instrument is

A 72×35 mm **B** 72×36 mm **C** 72 mm **D** $72 \div 35$ mm
E $72 \div 36$ mm

L32 A simple two-lens astronomical telescope has a magnifying power of 12.0 when used in normal adjustment. The focal length of the objective is 1.08 m. The focal length of the eyepiece is

A 1.2 m **B** 0.96 m **C** 0.54 m **D** 0.090 m **E** 0.081 m

L33 A ray of light is incident upon a plane mirror which is rotating at 10 rad s^{-1}. The reflected ray appears to rotate at

A $\sqrt{10}$ rad s^{-1} **B** $10 \div 2$ rad s^{-1} **C** 10 rad s^{-1} **D** 10×2 rad s^{-1}
E 10^2 rad s^{-1}

L34 When a simple camera is focused on a distant object, the distance from the lens to the film is found to be 40.0 mm. In order to focus an image on the film for an object which lies 0.54 m in front of the lens, the required displacement of the lens is

A zero
B 2.7 mm towards the film
C 3.2 mm towards the film
D 2.7 mm away from the film
E 3.2 mm away from the film

L35 In a pinhole camera, the effect of doubling the diameter of the hole from 0.5 mm to 1.0 mm is to

1 double the magnification of the image
2 worsen the chromatic aberration of the image
3 increase the blurring of the image caused by diffraction
4 cut the necessary exposure time to one-quarter of its previous value

L36 Long sight is commonly caused by the eyeball being rather shorter than normal along the axis of the lens. It could, in principle, also be caused by

1 a vitreous humour with too high a refractive index
2 a crystalline lens with too high a refractive index
3 a cornea which is not sufficiently curved
4 a crystalline lens with faces which are too sharply curved

L37 When the spectrum of an excited monatomic gas is examined in a prism spectrometer, the angular width of the spectral lines depends upon

1 the distance between the collimator slit and the source
2 the magnifying power of the telescope
3 the refractive index of the prism (for light giving the line under observation)
4 the width of the collimator slit

M GENERAL PHYSICS

Units

M1 The following are vector quantities:

1 acceleration **2** density **3** momentum **4** energy

M2 The following are scalar quantities:

1 speed **2** power **3** mass **4** weight

M3 A suitable unit for the measurement of pressure is

A $kg\,m^{-1}\,s^{-2}$ **B** $kg\,m^{-2}$ **C** $kg\,N^{-1}\,s^{-1}$ **D** $kg^2\,m^2\,s^{-2}$ **E** $kg\,m^{-2}\,s^{-2}$

M4 A suitable unit for the measurement of Young's modulus is

A $kg\,m^{-1}\,s^{-2}$ **B** $N\,m^2$ **C** $N\,m^2\,s^{-1}$ **D** $kg\,m^{-2}$ **E** $kg\,m^{-3}\,s^{-2}$

M5 Which of the following pairs have identical dimensions:

1 work and kinetic energy **2** momentum and force
3 moment of a force and moment of a couple
4 pressure and surface tension

M6 An athletics coach told his team 'Muscle times speed equals power!' What dimensions does he envisage for 'muscle'?

A L **B** ML^2T^{-2} **C** MT^{-2} **D** MLT^{-2} **E** M

M7 If $1\ g\,cm\,s^{-1} = x\ N\,s$, then the number x is equal to

A 1×10^{-5} **B** 6×10^{-4} **C** 3.6×10^{-3} **D** 1×10^{-1} **E** 3.6×10^{3}

M8 Suitable units for the universal constant of gravitation, *G*, are

A $kg\,m\,s^{-2}$ **B** $m\,s^{-2}$ **C** $N\,m^{-1}s$ **D** $kg\,m\,s^{-1}$ **E** $kg^{-1}\,m^{3}\,s^{-2}$

M9 The J s (joule second) could be a unit for

1 power
2 angular momentum
3 the universal constant of gravitation G
4 Planck's constant h

Graphs and errors

M10 A force F varies sinusoidally with time t as shown in the graph.

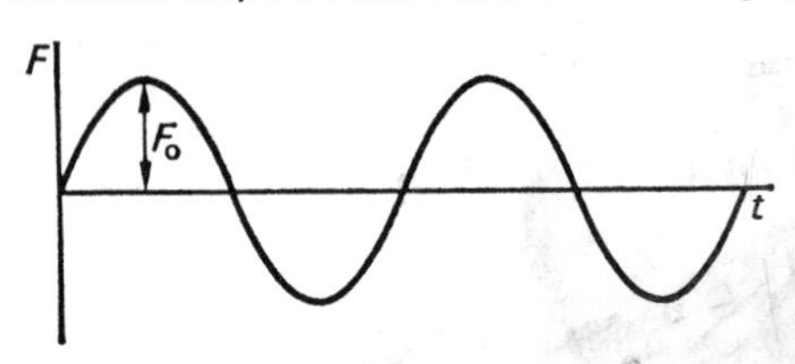

The average force is

A zero **B** $\frac{1}{\sqrt{2}}F_0$ **C** $\frac{1}{\pi}F_0$ **D** $2F_0$
E some other fraction of F_0

M11 The length l of a piece of wire is related to its temperature T by the equation $l = a(1 + bT)$, where a and b are constants. A series of experimental values is obtained for l and T and a graph of l (up) against T (along) is plotted.

1 The slope of the graph is ab
2 The intercept on the T axis is $-a/b$
3 The intercept on the l axis is a
4 The graph is not a straight line

M12 A convex lens is used to form a real image of a bright object on a screen. If

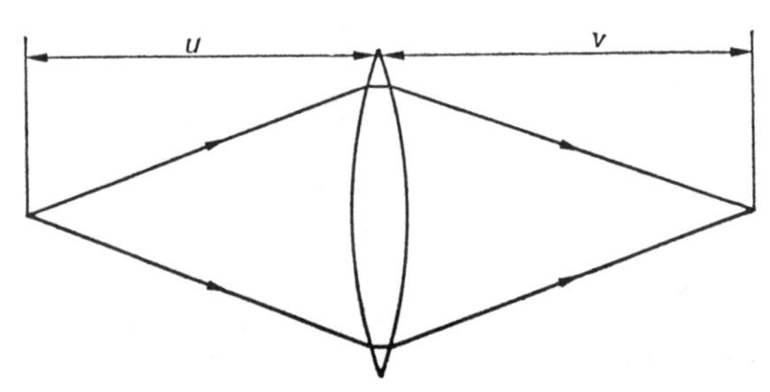

the object distance, u, and the image distance, v, are related by the equation $\frac{1}{u}+\frac{1}{v}=\frac{1}{f}$, where f is a constant, then in the graph shown the axes represent

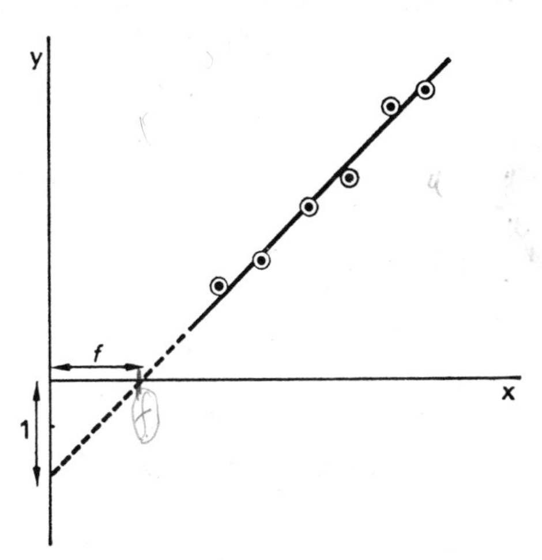

A uv for x, $u+v$ for y **B** u for x, u/v for y **C** $u-v$ for x, v/u for y
D $\frac{1}{u}$ for x, $u+v$ for y **E** $\frac{1}{u}$ for x, $\frac{1}{v}$ for y

M13 A circular flat coil of radius a carrying a current I produces a magnetic field which varies along the axis of the coil. The flux density, B, a distance x from the plane of the coil, is given by

$$B=\frac{kI}{(a^2+x^2)^{\frac{3}{2}}}$$

With constant I, values of B and x are measured and a graph plotted. A linear graph would be drawn if B were plotted against

A $(a^2+x^2)^{\frac{3}{2}}$ **B** a^2+x^2 **C** x^3 **D** $(a^2+x^2)^{-1}$ **E** $(a^2+x^2)^{-\frac{3}{2}}$

M14 The resistance, R, of a lamp bulb is thought to vary with the current, I, through the bulb according to a relation of the form

$$R=kI^{\frac{3}{2}}$$

where k is constant.

A linear graph would be obtained by plotting

A R against I **B** R against $\log I$ **C** R^2 against I **D** R^2 against I^3
E $\log R$ against I

M15 A piece of cardboard is cut out as shown and its centre of gravity located at G.

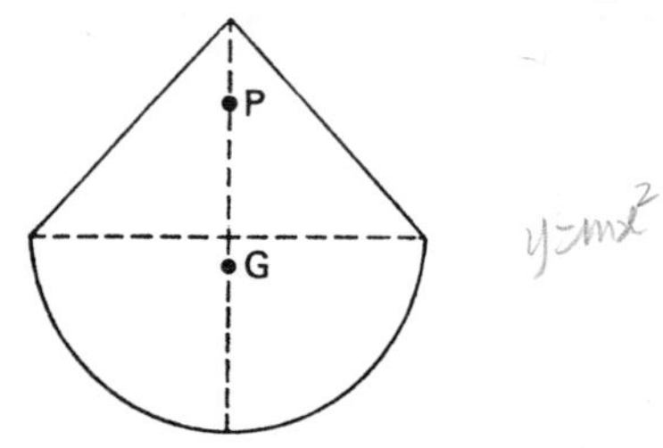

It is suspended about a horizontal axis through P and made to oscillate in its own plane. If $GP = h$ when the period is T then

$$T^2 = \frac{a}{h} + bh$$

where a and b are constants.

A linear graph could be obtained by plotting

1 h against T **2** log h against log T **3** T^2 against h
4 T^2h against h^2

M16 In an attempt to measure the diameter of a piece of wire, using a micrometer screw gauge, the following values were obtained:

Mean zero reading -0.06 ± 0.02 mm
Mean apparent diameter $+1.01 \pm 0.02$ mm

The diameter would be quoted as

A 1.07 ± 0.02 mm **B** 0.95 ± 0.04 mm **C** 1.07 ± 0.04 mm
D 0.95 ± 0.02 mm **E** 1.07 ± 0.00 mm

M17 Vernier calipers, reading to 0.1 mm, are used to find the internal diameter (10.0 ± 0.1 mm) and the external diameter (12.0 ± 0.1 mm) of a length of glass tubing. The mean wall thickness would be quoted, therefore, as

A 1.0 ± 0.2 mm **B** 2.0 ± 0.1 mm **C** 2.0 ± 0.2 mm **D** 1.0 ± 0.1 mm
E being indeterminate without the zero reading of the gauge

M18 The relative density of a metal, i.e. the ratio $\left(\frac{\text{density of the metal}}{\text{density of water}}\right)$ may be found by hanging a block of the metal from a spring balance and noting that in air the balance read 5.00 ± 0.05 N, while in water it read 4.00 ± 0.05 N.

The relative density would then be quoted as

A 5.00 ± 0.05 **B** 5.00 ± 0.10 **C** $5.00 \pm 5\%$ **D** $5.00 \pm 6\%$
E $5.00 \pm 11\%$

M19 To find the density of aluminium, the mass of a sheet of foil is found ($\pm 1\%$). Its length ($\pm 1\%$) and breadth ($\pm 1\%$) are both then found. Its mean thickness is found by folding it twice to give a stack of four sheets, the thickness of which is measured to be 11.2 ± 0.4 mm, and the zero reading of the screw gauge is recorded as $+1.2 \pm 0.4$ mm. The error to be quoted in the density is

A $\pm 3\%$ **B** $\pm 4\%$ **C** $\pm 5\%$ **D** $\pm 11\%$ **E** $\pm 35\%$

M20 In an experiment to measure the specific heat capacity, *c*, of aluminium in the form of a block, the following readings are made and the errors estimated to be those shown:

mass aluminium block = 1.01 kg
initial temperature of block = 18.4 ± 0.5 °C
final temperature of block = 31.0 ± 0.5 °C
rate of energy input to block = 52 ± 1 W
time for heating block = 215 s

The calculated value for *c* should be quoted as

A $(880 \pm 20)\ \mathrm{J\ kg^{-1}\ K^{-1}}$
B $(880 \pm 25)\ \mathrm{J\ kg^{-1}\ K^{-1}}$
C $(880 \pm 55)\ \mathrm{J\ kg^{-1}\ K^{-1}}$
D $(880 \pm 70)\ \mathrm{J\ kg^{-1}\ K^{-1}}$
E $(880 \pm 90)\ \mathrm{J\ kg^{-1}\ K^{-1}}$

Miscellaneous

M21 Which of the following statements is *far* from correct?

A A typical human life span is 10^9 s
B The Earth–Sun distance is 10^{11} m
C A nitrogen molecule has a mass of 5×10^{-26} kg
D The time for light to cross a human eyeball is 10^{-4} s
E The number of water molecules in a cup of coffee is 2×10^{23}

M22 Only one of the following statements is correct, the other four being wrong by at least an order of magnitude. Which statement is correct?

A In one year light travels about 10^{12} metre
B The frequency of an electromagnetic wave of wavelength 1500 m is about 2×10^8 Hz
C The mass of the Earth, which has an average density of about 5000 kg m^{-3}, is roughly 6×10^{24} kg
D The volume of a full grown man is about 2 m^3
E A lump of coal contains 10^{21} atoms

M23 The Moon M and the Sun S subtend roughly equal angles when viewed from the Earth E. We can deduce that

1 S and M have equal diameters
2 if S has a larger diameter than M then M is nearer to E than S is to E
3 E and S will subtend equal angles when viewed from M
4 during an eclipse of the Sun as seen from E, M will just cover S

M24 A pendulum clock consists of a massive lead sphere fixed to the end of a rod of brass which swings about a horizontal axis through its upper end. When the temperature is 20 °C the clock keeps time correctly. When the temperature falls to 0 °C

1 the clock will lose
2 the period of the pendulum will alter because the mass of the lead sphere changes
3 the period of the pendulum will alter because the weight of the lead sphere changes
4 the alteration in the period depends on the coefficient of linear expansion of brass

M25 The metacentre of a body is

A the point at which the mass of the body may be considered to be concentrated
B the point through which the pull of the Earth on the body always acts
C the point on a submerged vertical plane surface at which the resultant horizontal thrust of the fluid may be considered to act
D the point in a body displacing a fluid through which the Archimedes upthrust always acts
E a name given to the centre point of a planet

M26 A cardboard disc on an outer annulus of which is printed a series of 12 equally spaced black segments is placed on a gramophone turntable which rotates it steadily at 0.75 revolutions per second. When the disc is illuminated by a lamp which flashes with a frequency f, the black segments appear to be quite stationary. We can conclude that

A f *must* equal 3×12 Hz
B f *must* equal $\frac{3 \times 12}{2}$ Hz
C f *could* equal $\frac{4 \times 12}{3}$ Hz
D f *could* equal $\frac{3 \times 12}{4}$ Hz
E f *must* be greater than 12 Hz

M27 The graph represents an exponential decrease, the rate of decrease of y being proportional to $(y - y_0)$. The quantity y could be

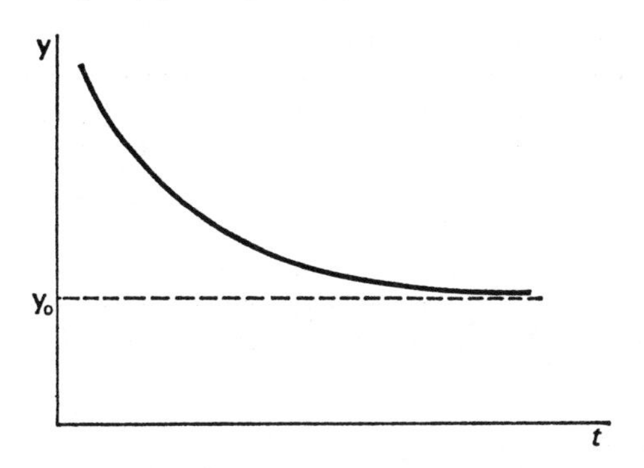

1 the current in a wire which was connected at $t = 0$ across a charged capacitor
2 the activity of a radioactive source which emits only α-particles
3 the speed of a space capsule as it moves away from the Earth after the rockets cease to burn
4 the temperature of a beaker of hot water in a large room

M28 The graph shown could, with a suitable scale on the y-axis, be used to represent

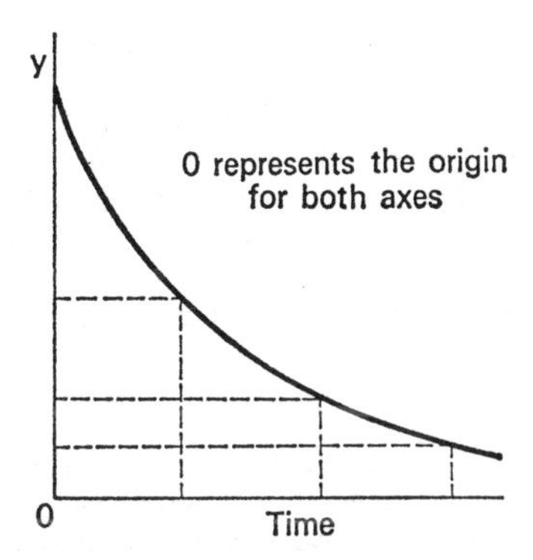

A the current in a circuit containing a cell, a resistor and an inductor when the cell is disconnected
B the absolute temperature of a hot body suspended in a steady flow of air
C the amplitude of the swing of a simple pendulum initially released at 30° to the vertical
D the number of disintegrated atoms in a piece of radioactive material
E the potential difference between two charged plates (which have no mutual inductance) when they are connected via a high value resistor